45771

F TECHNOLOGY

D0486792

CANTERBURY COLLEGE OF TECHNOLOGY
NEW DOVER

LIBRARY

CLASS No. 372.7 Bel.

BOOK No. 45771

BRIGHT IDEAS

Maths Projects

Written by David Bell

Published by Scholastic Publications Ltd,
Villiers House, Clarendon Avenue,
Leamington Spa, Warwickshire CV32 5PR

© 1992 Scholastic Publications Ltd

Written by David Bell
Edited by Juliet Gladston
Sub-edited by Catherine Baker
Illustrated by Lesley Smith
Front and back covers designed by Sue Limb
Photograph by Martyn Chillmaid
Typeset by Typesetters (Birmingham) Ltd
Printed in Great Britain by Loxley Brothers Ltd, Sheffield
Artwork by Norfolk House Graphic Design, Leicester

British Library Cataloguing in Publication Data
A catalogue record for this book is available from the British Library.

ISBN 0-590-53002-X

All rights reserved. This book is sold subject to the condition that it shall not, by way of trade or otherwise, be lent, hired out or otherwise circulated without the publisher's prior consent in any form of binding or cover other than that in which it is published and without a similar condition, including this condition, being imposed upon the subsequent purchaser.

No part of this publication may be reproduced, stored in a retrieval system, or transmitted, in any form or by any means, electronic, mechanical, photocopying, recording or otherwise, without the prior permission of the publisher, except where photocopying for educational purposes within a school or other educational establishment is expressly permitted in the text.

Contents

Introduction

In primary schools the National Curriculum (including RE) is divided into ten separate subjects. However, from the outset, it has been stressed that teachers and schools are free to organise the curriculum in whatever way they think is most appropriate for the children they teach. For that reason, many primary schools have maintained a cross-curricular approach on the grounds that it best reflects the way in which primary-aged children see and learn about the world. Additionally, cross-curricular approaches have been seen as an efficient way of teaching and learning, given the limited amount of time available to cover the extensive demands of the National Curriculum.

Even in schools that have promoted cross-curricular approaches, mathematics has often been taught separately. Many teachers have felt that because of its central importance as a core subject and the assumed sequential nature of mathematical learning, mathematics needs to be considered separately. Therefore, most schools will follow either a commercial maths scheme or a school-devised scheme based on the National Curriculum programme of study.

Clearly, there is merit in this approach as it reflects the central position mathematics has in the National Curriculum. Also, many teachers feel more confident teaching mathematics as a discrete element of the curriculum. This book is not intended to challenge such an approach, but to increase the opportunities extended to children for undertaking mathematical work. The book is based on the following assumptions:

- Although the study of mathematics is interesting in itself, it is essentially a tool for everyday life. Therefore, in learning about mathematics, children need to see it used in day-to-day situations.
- Real-life contexts draw upon the mathematical knowledge which children bring to school and which they often use independently of what they are taught. Thus, relating school work to practical examples will encourage children to use a range of mathematical skills and strategies.
- Children can extend their mathematical knowledge by working with other children and sharing skills and experiences. Discussion and co-operation will allow children to see mathematical possibilities that they might fail to see on their own.
- The six approaches to effect mathematical teaching which were identified in the 1982 Cockcroft Report remain valid even in the context of the National Curriculum. Five of the six elements are covered in a cross-curricular

approach, namely: discussion between teacher and pupils and between pupils themselves; appropriate practical work; consolidation of basic skills; problem solving; investigational work.

• If the cross-curricular approach is educationally valid because it reflects how young children see the world, then it does not make sense for mathematics to be considered always in isolation. Children should be encouraged to transfer their mathematical knowledge into other areas of the curriculum and vice versa.

USING THIS BOOK IN SCHOOL

This book can be used to support mathematical teaching and learning in a number of ways.

• It could provide the mathematical element for a range of popular classroom topics. For example, if you are working on a topic on sport, there are a number of mathematical dimensions available to suit a range of ages and abilities.

• It could be used as the basis for short mathematical topics which draw less upon other subjects, concentrating instead on drawing out all the mathematical possibilities.

• It could provide practical examples to use in mainstream mathematics work based around a commercial or school maths scheme. These activities could be drawn from various chapters and used independently.

• It could be used as a resource bank for providing problem solving activities which the children could complete over a period of time.

• It could be used as a book of 'one-off' ideas which children could undertake when most of their structured work has been completed.

Essentially, the book is intended to be flexible enough to be used in whatever way is most appropriate for you.

THE CONTENT OF THE BOOK

This book is divided into eight activity chapters. Each chapter follows a popular classroom theme which could be developed for children at either Key Stage 1 or Key Stage 2. The same format is used to describe each activity.

• The age range indicates the main target group for the activities. In general terms, the activities are divided into three age groups; five to seven, seven to nine and nine to eleven. In many cases, the possible age range is wider and teachers will find ways of adapting the activity as appropriate.

• The group size indicates the number of children who can undertake an activity. Again, this can be adapted to suit individual needs.

• The 'What you need' section specifies the resources that are required for the activity.

• The 'What to do' section provides a brief description of the activity itself and what the children have to do to complete it. In some cases the activity will consist of a number of separate tasks.

● The follow-up outlines the most direct and logical additional activities to accompany the main activity. However, there will probably be a range of other activities which can also be used as a continuation of the main work.

Some activities also have photocopiable worksheets to accompany them. The activities will explain how these are to be used, and they can be found at the end of the book. At the end of every chapter there are also some ideas for classroom display. These are intended to provide ideas on ways to display mathematical work related to the chapter theme. It is assumed that these ideas will form part of any wider topic display that might be established. The purpose of including this section is to encourage teachers to see mathematical work as something which can be visually exciting, and which is worth displaying and celebrating in the same way as a piece of writing or a painting.

Finally, at the end of the book, an attainment target chart outlines the relationship of each activity to the revised maths National Curriculum attainment targets. This will be an invaluable resource when planning a work programme that relates directly to the National Curriculum.

THE WAY FORWARD

The ideas in this book can be expanded and developed, and new activities can be devised for each theme. There are also, of course, many other themes that could be used for a maths project. However you decide to use the book, it will only succeed if you are committed to providing the widest possible range of mathematical activities for the children in your care.

1. Shopping

Shops and shopping are familiar to children before they come to school. Most children will have accompanied their parents around local shops from a very young age and will be familiar with the vocabulary and routines of shopping. The vast majority of schools offer shopping activities to their children, but these are often of limited scope and confined to the younger classes. As a mathematical topic, shopping can be extended throughout the school with the types of shops and activities becoming progressively more varied as children get older. The topic can also be introduced throughout the year, although it is often popular in the build-up to Christmas as thoughts turn to buying presents. The topic of shopping can also be popular in the summer term if there are opportunities to take children out for a visit to the local shops.

1. At the sales

Age range
Five to seven.

Group size
Pairs.

What you need
Empty food packaging such as cereal packets and juice cartons; labels with '5p off', '10p off', '20p off' and so on; toy money, paper, pencils.

What to do
As children begin to consolidate their understanding of simple subtraction, let them work together to calculate the discount prices of various items. Before working out the discount, of course, the children will need to price

the goods. It is best if you set pricing limits beforehand, so that the calculations will be within their capabilities. For example, you might say that no item should cost more than 50p. The prices will therefore reflect the stage the children are at, rather than the actual shop prices.

Once each item has been priced by the children they can use the discount cards, such as '5p off' or '10p off'. The prices on these cards can be within limits that you have set, or they can be set by the children themselves. Each child should take a turn at putting a discount card beside each priced item, and then his or her partner should try to work out the new price.

You might like to add a new dimension for both children in the pairs, by saying that 10p has been taken off everything in the store or, perhaps, 20p has been added to everything.

Ideally, all the activities suggested here should be done using toy money so that children become familiar with sorting out the correct money.

Follow-up
As the children become more proficient at calculating discounts you could introduce concepts such as 'all items are half price'. More advanced children could also look at percentage increases or decreases in price.

2. The shoe shop

Age range
Five to seven.

Group size
Various.

What you need
Items for creating a shoe shop such as soft seats, shoe boxes, mirrors, a stool, display shelves for shoe boxes, old shoes, a foot measure.

What to do
A shoe shop is an excellent shop for children to create as it presents a range of mathematical possibilities.

Each child can take turns to act as the shopkeeper and be responsible for measuring the feet of other children. Ask them to consider why very accurate measurements are so important.

Have a range of shoes of different sizes on display so that the shopkeepers can display estimation skills as they guess the likely shoe size of their customers.

As shoes are offered for the customer's consideration, both the shopkeeper and the customer can ensure that they know their right from their left.

If the chidren are dealing with actual prices, they could consider why so many shoes cost £X.99.

The children could use calculators to work out the change required from larger amounts tendered, although they could also be encouraged to try and work out the change for themselves by rounding up to the nearest pound.

Encourage the children to keep records of the most popular shoes in the shop. They could display these in the form of 'feet graphs'. They could also sort shoes into different categories for display in the shop; for example, sport shoes, shoes for dress wear, winter shoes and so on. The children can establish their own sets and see where they overlap.

Follow-up
Work on shoes and feet can be extended in a variety of ways.
● The volume of shoes could be investigated using marbles as a 'standard' unit.
● Tread patterns could be investigated for symmetrical designs.
● Look at laces: can the children find different ways of tying them?
● Shoe boxes could be designed and made for specialist shoes like wellington boots, flippers and roller skates.

3. The sweet shop

Age range
Five to seven.

Group size
Various.

What you need
Items for creating the sweet shop, including materials for making sweets (for example, Plasticine in crêpe paper, wrapped pieces of card, card 'lollies' on sticks and so on); jars; bucket scales and weights.

What to do
A real sweet shop is full of bright colours in interesting combinations. The items that the children create to fill their sweet shop will provide opportunities to discuss repeat patterns and symmetry. They could base their sweet patterns and designs on patterns they know from real sweets and chocolate bars.

Once the play sweets have been made and the storage jars filled, the children can then weigh out different amounts of sweets such as 100g, 200g or 500g using the scales, but they should always be encouraged to estimate the quantities before weighing them accurately. They should do this by taking a bundle of sweets in one hand and a scale weight in the other hand and trying to feel the correct weight.

Let the children make up price lists, saying that 1kg of a certain sort of sweet costs 20p, for example. Set problems like: 'Buy 2kg of mini-bars. How much does it cost?' Criteria for buying sweets such as '4 for 1p' can lead to simple multiplication, whereas 'Give me 12 sweets' leads to simple subtraction work.

Follow-up
● Encourage the children to make judgements about the relative values of sweets on sale in the shops. Is it 'better value' if you get more sweets in the packet, or if the sweets last longer, or are the ones you enjoy most the best value? Help the children to see that judgements about value depend on what you are looking for.
● Use the 'sweets' theme to undertake other interesting activities. For example, ask the children to use a stopwatch to see how long a fruit gum will last or, using three boxes of Smarties, compile a frequency chart and sort by colour.

4. The clothes shop

Age range
Five to nine.

Group size
Various.

What you need
Items for creating a clothes shop such as old clothes, hanging rails, coat-hangers, a hat-stand, a mirror, a tape-measure and so on.

What to do
Setting up a clothes shop is usually quite easy, as most classrooms have a dressing-up box. The first job the children have to do is to sort the clothes into the different sizes. They can begin by estimating the sizes, and check by reading the labels on the clothes. They might then think about how the clothes are going to be displayed. Will all the sports clothes be displayed together or will the clothes be grouped according to size?

When the customers arrive at the shop they can be measured up. The children can take a range of different measurements, for example, chest size, inside leg length, head size if a hat is being bought, and so on. When the children have done this two or three times they should be able to make sensible estimates of sizes and provide appropriate clothes for the customers to try on without having to take measurements. To make this a more realistic activity, it is probably better that the shop only stocks children's clothes.

Some customers might want to purchase fabrics to design their own clothes. Have some rolls of old fabric available so that the correct lengths can be measured and cut. The children could look at clothes patterns, and perhaps the shop could offer a design and measuring service. The children can decide how the fabric is to be costed. Is it to be per square metre? If so, how much will different amounts cost? How do they estimate the cost of a piece of fabric which is not a full metre or a simple fraction of a full metre?

Follow-up
● The children could carry out a survey of favourite clothes and colours.
● If there are opportunities for the children to sew or knit, this can generate simple mathematical activities such as observing patterns and tesselations, counting the number of stitches in a row, and following a sequence of instructions.

5. At the supermarket

Age range
Seven to nine.

Group size
Up to four.

What you need
Pencils, clipboards, photocopiable page 111, calculators.

What to do
Arrange a trip to the local supermarket and, with the manager's permission, set the children on a maths trail around the shop. Ask them to find all the measuring equipment in the store, listing the names and identifying what the items are used for. They could also consider the degree of accuracy given by each piece of equipment. For example, why is there a bucket scale for

the customer to use at the self-service fruit and vegetable stall, but a digital scale at the checkout? They could find out how regularly such equipment is tested for accuracy.

The children could find out what are the best bargains of the week, working out the biggest reductions in terms of money or percentages. They might also look for the cheapest and dearest items in the store and work out the difference between the two prices.

Give the children a list of items, and ask them to find out which brand of each product offers the best value for money. To do this they will need to look at price and weight. But how can they measure quality? Is price always indicative of quality? Perhaps they could ask some customers who come to buy the items why they made the choice they did.

Ask the children to investigate the checkouts. What methods of payment are accepted? If bar coding is used, can they find out how it works?

Finally, the children might undertake a survey of the people who visit the store. Photocopiable page 111 suggests some questions that could be asked. The results can then be entered into a computer and analysed, and a report can be written for the shop. The report could include the percentage of shoppers who come once a week or once a month, and a summary of the reasons why shoppers choose to shop there.

Follow-up
● Having visited a large supermarket, organise a visit to a local small shop and compare the two.
● The children could write to some of the other larger shops in the area and collect and analyse statistics, such as the total number of people who visit the store, the number of people who work in the store and the store's annual turnover.

6. Birthday lists

Age range
Seven to eleven.

Group size
Pairs.

What you need
Pencils, paper, calculators, shopping catalogues.

What to do
Ask the children to write simple biographies for each member of a make-believe family of three or four people. They should include the age and hobbies or interests of each person. Ask them to imagine that each member of the family has a birthday coming up and that they have a set amount of money to spend on each of them. Using the shopping catalogues and the calculators, the children can make a list of presents

which would be likely to reflect the age and interests of each member of the family. You could add certain complications which would involve a degree of choice. For example, you might say that over the year, the family has allocated £100 to spend on all the birthdays, but there are other priorities to be considered as well, such as spending money for the holiday or the upkeep of the garden. You might also say that the shopping catalogue needs to be compared with other catalogues or prices in the shops to ensure the best value for money.

Follow-up
• The children could create present lists for their friends based on what they know about them. They might be given an amount of money to plan with, but subsequently find the amount of money reduced. What decisions would then have to be made?
• Shopping catalogues can introduce the children to division as they think about paying by instalments. For example, how much would an item priced £19.99 cost per week over ten weeks?

7. Shops in the past

Age range
Nine to eleven.

Group size
Pairs.

What you need
Old local directories such as Kelly's Directory.

What to do
Local street directories are usually available in the library. These contain a list of the people who lived in a street at different times in the past. If you can identify a street which has had shops in it for many years, the children can undertake a number of mathematical activities. For example, they could work out how long the shops have been there, creating a time line to show when the shops changed owners and when they changed character.

If there are any gaps in the information the children could consider the likelihood of the shops having remained the same. If rents are given in pre-decimal money, they can identify the main coins and their relative values. Can the children work out what the rents would have been in decimal money? If maps of the area are enclosed, the children could draw scale plans of the same area today, identifying where the different shops are and what they are currently being used for.

8. Shopping survey

Age range
Nine to eleven.

Group size
Pairs.

What you need
A clipboard, photocopiable page 112.

What to do
Most schools are situated near a shopping centre offering a range of goods and services. Photocopiable page 112 will assist the children to identify the range of services on offer in their local shopping centre, how long they have been there, when they are available and who uses them. However, the children will have to visit the shopping centre on a number of occasions to find out the times at which the shops are most popular and the age range of the people using them. They will need to design their own data collection sheets and decide what times of the day they wish to visit the centre. Early morning, mid-morning, lunch time and mid-afternoon are likely to be good survey times. If, however, it is not possible to visit at different times, the survey could concentrate on one particular time. Consult with the local shopkeepers to find out what time is likely to be best.

When the results are brought back to the school, enter them into a database and prepare an exhibition based on the data collected. Use a line graph to show the number of customers in the shops at different times of the day. A pie-chart could show the breakdown of age groups using the shopping centre. Ultimately, the children could invite the shopkeepers to visit the class, and inform them of their conclusions, making recommendations based on their research.

Follow-up
Undertake this survey at different times of the year and compare the results. For example, are there fewer elderly people using the shops in the winter?

9. The post office

Age range
Nine to eleven.

Group size
Various.

What you need
Items for creating the post office such as a counter, toy money, materials to make cheque books, pension books, television licence books and so on.

What to do
A post office is an excellent shop for older children to create because they will be familiar with some of the services offered; for example, postage services, licences, banking facilities and so on. Begin by making a list of the services provided by a post office and, if possible, look at examples of the books and materials available. Let the children create their own types of allowances and identify rates of payment for such things as driving licences, television licences and pensions.

The children could establish their own internal postal system within the school. Different classrooms and teachers could be allocated a different postcode; the children could perhaps talk to the local post office to find out about the logical structure of postcodes. The children will also need to establish rates of postage for letters and parcels of different sizes. They could use the current post office rates or make up their own. What sort of weighing equipment will be required? Will standard school scales be appropriate? They should also look at air mail services and work out routes, times and costs for letters going to different parts of the world.

Don't forget to tell the children about Girobank so that they can work out interest rates in percentages and calculate how much interest customers are entitled to.

Follow-up
Visit the local post office and talk to the postmen and postwomen about their routes. Ask the children to estimate how long it takes them to deliver all the letters and parcels on their routes. They could set up a calculation based on how long it takes them to walk off the street and post a letter through a letterbox. How accurate is the children's estimate?

10. The shopping centre

Age range
Five to eleven.

Group size
Various.

What you need
A large hall area set out with various shops, other accessories of a shopping centre such as benches, newspaper stalls and so on; carrier bags for each child; a quantity of toy money for each child.

What to do
Setting up a shopping centre which can be the focus of the whole school's mathematical activities is an excellent way to practise a whole range of skills. Such an event can last anything up to a week and will require careful planning and co-ordination. Various practicalities need to be considered, such as making alternative arrangements for PE lessons and school dinners, if the hall is normally used for these activities. It is therefore often better to hold such an event in the summer so that these other activities can take place outside.

Shopping timetables need to be arranged and all staff need to be aware of the aims and objectives of the event. Every class in the school should set up its own shop, which can be staffed on a rota basis by children from that class. Set the hall up like a proper shopping centre with walkways and shops that look as much as possible like their real-life equivalents.

When the shopping centre is open, the day can be split into a number of sessions with groups of children coming into the hall during each session. Mix up the age ranges and allow the children to wander freely around the shopping centre with their toy money. It is also worth having one or two shops such as a café or a paper shop where real money can be spent. If you have a bank as one of your services, the children could be encouraged to open a pretend bank account and be issued with a cheque book and credit card.

To obtain the maximum benefit from such an event, the children who are acting as the shopkeepers need to ensure that they know what goes on in their shop's real-life counterpart. If a class is running a travel agency, for example, the children need to know the procedures involved in booking a holiday. Make sure that there are plenty of other adults around the hall to engage in active role-play with the children.

The following shops could be set up:
• Five- to seven-year-olds: toy shop, shoe shop, sweet shop and greengrocer.
• Seven- to nine-year-olds: clothes shop, grocer's shop, café, bakery and sports shop.
• Nine- to eleven-year-olds: estate agency, travel agency, bank, post office and chemist.

Classroom display ideas

- If at all possible, every primary classroom should have a space set aside for a class shop. Even if this is only a table and a few simple objects, children will gain practical experience in using money and undertaking a range of other mathematical activities. Using the ideas in this chapter, the basic space can be built on in many different ways.

- Always have available a set of standard signs that can be brought out at different times, such as '5p off', 'Everything half price', '10% increase' and so on.
- Create a large wall display (or, even better, a model) of the inside of a shop. Include labels for all the places in which mathematics will be used.
- Create a giant shopping list on the wall showing the children's ten favourite items at the supermarket. How much would it cost to buy all the items on the list?
- Have a shopping bag displayed with various items in it, all separately priced. Change the items regularly and ask the children to work out the total cost of the items.
- Make a display of items that cost less than 10p, 20p or 50p.
- Make a display of supermarket packets, naming the shape of each box. Display the children's alternative packaging for the same products.
- Display the results of your shopping survey in detail. How many kinds of graphs can be used? Ask the children to write out the findings shown in the graphs.
- Display a collection of different kinds of receipts. You could make a shop mural out of them.

Links with other curriculum areas

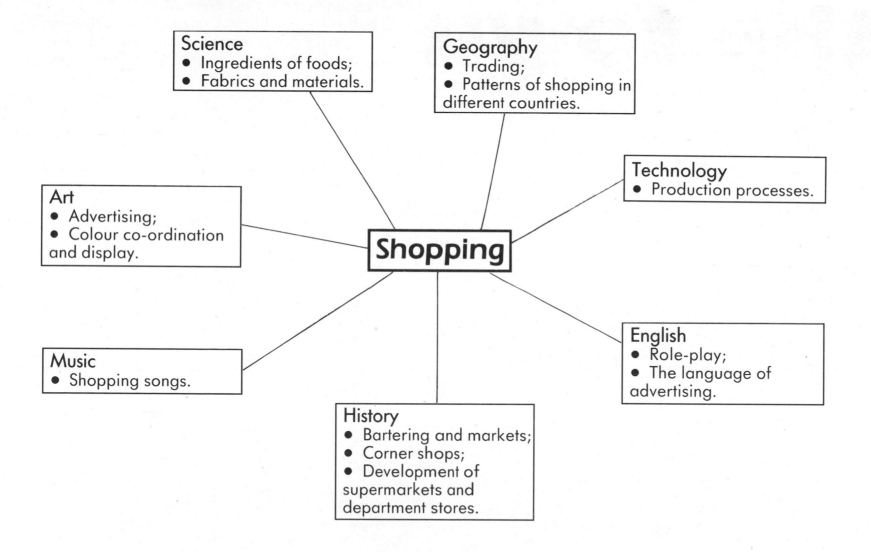

Science
- Ingredients of foods;
- Fabrics and materials.

Geography
- Trading;
- Patterns of shopping in different countries.

Technology
- Production processes.

Art
- Advertising;
- Colour co-ordination and display.

Shopping

English
- Role-play;
- The language of advertising.

Music
- Shopping songs.

History
- Bartering and markets;
- Corner shops;
- Development of supermarkets and department stores.

2. Maths in the town

Developing children's awareness of the local environment is a common aim in primary schools. The history and geography of the locality provide a rich source of inspiration for topics. As children are taken out and about either as a class or in small groups, there are many opportunities to look at the town from a mathematical perspective. The great advantage of this theme is that it takes mathematics out of the classroom and encourages children to see mathematics all around them.

1. Big and small

Age range
Five to six.

Group size
The whole class or small groups.

What you need
No special requirements.

What to do
When children first start school, they need to be encouraged to develop mathematical language, using words such as 'tall', 'short', 'wide', 'narrow', 'long' and so on. It is only after such concepts have been grasped that standard units can be introduced.

Take the children out on a short walk around the local area and encourage them to use as much mathematical vocabulary as possible. For example, ask them to make comparisons between houses. Which house is the taller? Which is the tallest building in the area? As you go up and down different streets and roads, ask the children to decide which road they think is the longest. As they

come to doors and openings, ask which ones are wide and which are narrow. This can be extended into simple counting activities; for example, counting the number of doors or windows in a house.

When the children come back into school, set them some questions which they can discuss and answer in simple sentences.
- Where was the tallest house they saw on their walk and what did it look like?
- Of all the roads and streets that they walked in, which was the longest? Can the children think of a longer street or road nearby?
- Can they describe the thinnest building they saw during their visit?

Follow-up
Trips like this, and subsequent work in the classroom using non-standard units, eventually lead to the introduction of simple standard units such as metres and centimetres. It would not be possible for young children to measure the height of buildings or length of streets, but they could be set the task of deciding how such items could be measured and which units of measurements would be used.

2. The postman calls

Age range
Five to seven.

Group size
Up to four.

What you need
Addressed envelopes.

What to do
Ask the children to bring in a collection of old, empty, addressed envelopes from home. They could then look at different categories of letters, such as those with typed addresses or those with handwritten addresses, and formulate a hypothesis about letters which come in typewritten envelopes, for example, that they tend to be formal business letters or bills.

When you have collected together a large bundle of envelopes, put them into a sack and ask a group of children to estimate how many there are. Then they can sort the letters into bundles for each address. If the majority of the children in the class live in neighbouring streets, ask each group of children to plan a delivery route. The different routes could sent to the local post office, with a letter asking what criteria they use to devise the same route for their postmen and postwomen. If possible, take the groups of children out and let them time how long it takes them to walk their planned delivery route. Compare the different routes of the groups in the class, and see which one is the shortest and which one is the longest. Older children could draw out their routes.

When the children are out, ask them to look at the odd and even numbers on houses. Why are houses numbered in this way? What would happen if houses did not have numbers on them?

Follow-up
Invite a postman into school to describe how he does his job. He could describe the different routes he takes and how his letters are sorted for him. If possible, arrange a visit to the local sorting office to see how the letters are sorted on a large scale.

3. Around the houses

Age range
Six to nine.

Group size
Pairs.

What you need
Photocopiable page 113.

What to do
Take the children out on a walk and ask them to look for a range of flat and three-dimensional shapes in the environment. You could give the children a list of shapes and ask them to find as many as possible. Children may confuse flat and three-dimensional shapes, for example, calling a cube a square, and if they do, this allows you to point out the difference between them.

Follow up the walk by asking the children to use photocopiable page 113, which provides a number of basic shapes, to draw sketches of things they have seen in the local environment.

Follow-up
• The children could go on to identify right-angled corners in flat and three-dimensional shapes.
• Photocopiable page 113 can also be used in different settings, such as the classroom or the home.

4. Town trail

Age range
Seven to nine.

Group size
Pairs.

What you need
Photocopiable page 114, a trundle wheel.

What to do
Photocopiable page 114 provides a simple map with a scale box, showing a typical local neighbourhood. It can be used in a number of different ways. For example, the children could estimate the shortest route between two points. Ask them how they would find out what the actual distance was between these two points. They could then go out into their own local neighbourhood and put together a sketch map of the streets. How would they measure the length of the streets? They could use the trundle wheel and then work out a scale.

Although their maps might not be particularly accurate, it is important that the children gather their own measurements and then scale them down. If this is too difficult, give the children larger pieces of paper and let them scale up the map on photocopiable page 114.

Follow-up
Introduce a range of Ordnance Survey maps; for example, 1:25,000 and 1:50,000. As the children's map-making skills become more sophisticated, they could use the format of the Ordnance Survey maps as they design their own.

5. Paving shapes

Age range
Seven to nine.

Group size
Individuals.

What you need
Tape-measures, squared paper.

What to do
Paving stones are always interesting. What shapes can the children see in them? Are they squares or rectangles, or some other shape? What is their perimeter and area? You can introduce the idea of tessellation, as most paving consists of tessellating shapes, but the children could also identify paving stones that do not conform to this pattern such as paving stones in garden patio areas.

When the children come back to the classroom, they can use squared paper to draw scale drawings of the arrangements of paving stones they have seen.

Follow-up
● The children could also look at patterns in walls and buildings.
● Can they think of any natural patterns in the environment, such as in flowers and plants?

6. Road traffic survey

Age range
Seven to nine.

Group size
Pairs.

What you need
Photocopiable page 115.

What to do
Children are often asked to undertake traffic surveys without being given any real reason for doing so. It is important to ask the children why they might need to have such data, and how the data could be used. They might want to consult the council's road traffic or engineering departments or contact the local police station to see how they could use such information. The school governors might also be interested in the information because it would help them to provide information to parents.

Let the children use photocopiable page 115 for a fixed period of time. For comparative purposes it would be better to have data from three different times in the day, reflecting patterns of movement in and out of the school. If you have access to a computer database, this would allow the information to be manipulated in a number of ways. Again, ask the children what they think the important questions are. They may suggest the following:
- What are the busiest and quietest times of the day?
- What kind of traffic is most commonly seen on the roads?
- What is the ratio of cars to other vehicles?
- On average, how many vehicles pass the recording point every minute?

Try to ensure that the children see the relationship between mathematical and statistical work and the decisions that people make.

7. Maths trail

Age range
Seven to eleven.

Group size
Two or three.

What you need
Clipboards, paper.

What to do
Mathematics is all around us, and a 'maths trail' around the local environment can lead to a heightened awareness of numbers in day-to-day use. This activity is

best done without setting too many specific tasks. Give the children a general brief and say that you want them to find as many things as they can in the local neighbourhood connected with mathematics. If you ask them to gather basic data they can then analyse it when they get back to the classroom. It is likely that they will very quickly think of house numbers and signs in shops which identify prices. Ask them to consider shapes too. What flat and three-dimensional shapes do they see in the local environment?

Direction is another good theme. The children could look at arrows pointing left and right on road signs and markings. Cars, too, provide an excellent source of mathematical information. What information can be gleaned from a car number plate? How long has the tax disc to go before the expiry date? What does '1.6' or '1.8' mean on a car?

The children could look for angles on buildings. Can they find five right angles, five acute angles and five obtuse angles? They could also make sketches of the buildings and find lines of symmetry.

There are many more objects that the children could be asked to count. How many clocks can they find outside? What about looking at timetables for buses and trains? It is always interesting to see how far the children stretch the definition of mathematics. The wider the better!

Follow-up
When the children return to the classroom, they can use reference books to find out some background information about car number plates or road numbers. They could manipulate the house numbers they have recorded. For example, what happens if they multiply together the house numbers of adjacent houses?

8. Around the block

Age range
Eight to eleven.

Group size
Two or three.

What you need
A stop-watch, local maps.

What to do
Identify a reasonable circular walk starting and finishing at the school, and discuss it with the children. They could then draw their own diagrams of the planned walk and see how far these match with local maps.

The children then need to estimate how long it would take them to walk this route. To do this they first need to agree certain ground rules, such as the pace at which they are going to walk and whether or not they are going to take any short-cuts. Encourage the children not to make wild guesses, but to use information they already have, such as the time it takes them or their friends to walk a similar route home. Each pair or group of children should then make their estimate and write it down. They can check their estimates by taking a stop-watch and walking the route together with an adult helper or parent. When the children come back, they can compare their estimate with the actual time and examine the range of estimates.

Follow-up
• Older children could work out how far above or below the actual time their estimate was in percentage terms.
• Repeat the exercise using different routes. Does the children's estimating become more accurate?

9. Treasure hunt

Age range
Eight to eleven.

Group size
Up to four.

What you need
Local maps and reference books, calculators.

What to do
A topic on the local environment almost inevitably has a historical dimension, and this can involve many opportunities for mathematical work as well. The age of

buildings is a good place to begin. Some buildings will have a date carved in stone or on a tile on the exterior, and this can be used to work out how old the building is. Other buildings will yield clues in their architecture, and children should be encouraged to estimate the age of the buildings. Don't allow them to make wild guesses. Ask them to justify the estimates that they make. Reference books will be another source of information, and again the children can calculate the age of the buildings using the data they find.

If the children have access to an older building and a more modern equivalent (for example, houses built in the 1930s and 1980s) they could make some measurements and look at average room sizes. Why might these have changed over time?

What about historical artefacts? A visit to a local museum would allow the children to group objects and artefacts by age; for example, more than 50 years old but less than 100 years old. Local historical records might also throw up interesting facts. What was the average size of a family in a local street one hundred years ago? How far did people have to travel to work?

Finally, don't forget that local churchyards are an excellent source of mathematical as well as historical work. Churches themselves are full of interesting regular and symmetrical shapes. Don't just consider the mathematics; think, too, about the reasons. If you can, look at some very old gravestones. What centuries do they come from? How old were people when they died? What was the most common cause of death, if known?

Follow-up
The school itself may well be an interesting source of historical study. The children could examine old log books and registers and prepare a time line to show some of the most notable happenings in the school's life.

10. A new service

Age range
Ten to eleven.

Group size
Up to four or individuals.

What you need
Local maps, calculators, data collection sheets.

What to do
Children are usually vociferous in complaining about services which are lacking locally, from a certain kind of shop to a play facility. Set them the task of working out their own plan of campaign, from assessing a need to presenting a proposed solution. It is always better to ask them first to identify the stages they will have to go through. However, if they are having trouble doing this, you might want to use the following list.

● Stage 1: market research. The children need to find out what services or facilities are wanted. They could set up interviews with other children in the class or school. They will have to design a data collection sheet and then present their findings in a graphical format. A pie chart could be a useful form of presentation.

● Stage 2: identify an option. You might prefer each group to identify an option, or you may have just one for the whole class, broken down into different stages. The children need to work out a plan of action, and devise a decision tree diagram to represent the different choices.

● Stage 3: gather the information. This will depend on the option the children choose, but it might involve a range of activities. They may have to use local maps to identify a site for their proposal. They could contact the local council or estate agency to get costings for land. They could work out what professional services would be needed, for example, solicitors and surveyors, and cost this out. They might write to local builders and equipment manufacturers to get prices.

● Stage 4: present a proposal. The children will need to make scale plans, and three-dimensional models would also help. The children will need to decide how best to present their financial information. Perhaps they could design a glossy prospectus outlining their proposal and send it to the local newspaper, council, MP and so on. The children could log and collate the different responses they receive. You never know, something might just come of their proposal!

An idea like this overlaps with just about every other area of the curriculum. The best links are between mathematics and technology, as children have to identify a need, generate a design proposal, make a model and then evaluate the outcome. This could be a running theme throughout a local environment topic.

Classroom display ideas

- Create a three-dimensional model of the local area using boxes and other junk materials. Ensure as far as possible that the buildings are in scale.
- Make a display of the different envelopes that come into the children's homes over a week. Using the postmarks, find out which has come furthest.
- Create a wall display to show the different shaped paving stones and brickwork patterns found in the locality. Have these displays in a tessellated or non-tessellated form and try to create the different textures through paints and other art materials.
- Across a classroom wall, re-create the local shopping centre. Below each shop, have a summary of the data collected as part of the work done with photocopiable page 112.

- Put a local map on the wall, with the homes of each of the children identified. Find out the time it takes each child to get to school and display the average time.
- Create a display of the mathematics found on the 'maths trail' (see page 28). This could include road signs, house numbers, shop signs and so on.
- Create a large block graph summarising the results of the road traffic survey (see page 27). Each type of vehicle could be displayed, with the number of times it was seen over a given period. Remember to make sure that block graphs (and any graphs displayed) are labelled correctly.
- If a need has been identified for a new service (see page 31), display the process from beginning to end. Include the results of the initial market research, the design proposals and models, the costings and any correspondence sent or received by the children.
- Build a large-scale three-dimensional church and churchyard and highlight all the areas of mathematical investigation to be found there, including gravestones, windows, doors, spires, towers and so on.

Links with other curriculum areas

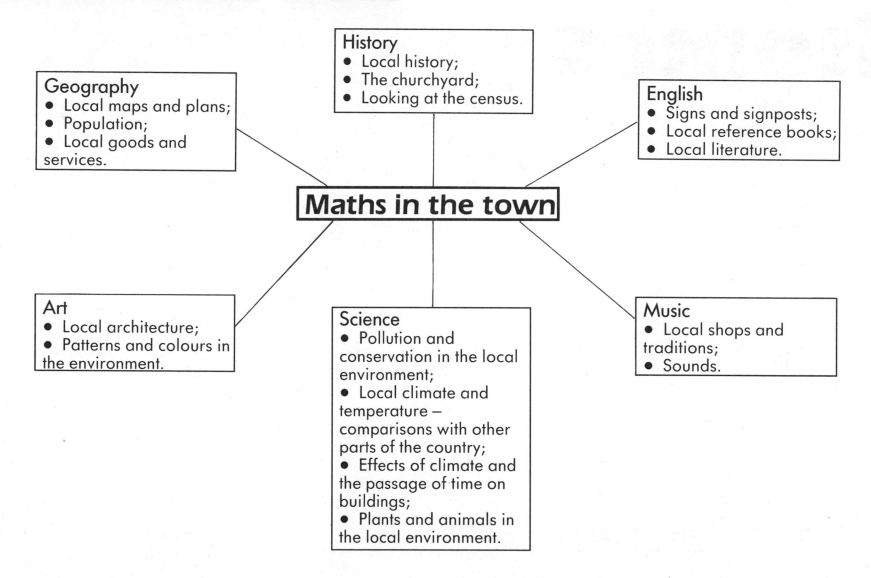

Geography
- Local maps and plans;
- Population;
- Local goods and services.

History
- Local history;
- The churchyard;
- Looking at the census.

English
- Signs and signposts;
- Local reference books;
- Local literature.

Maths in the town

Art
- Local architecture;
- Patterns and colours in the environment.

Science
- Pollution and conservation in the local environment;
- Local climate and temperature – comparisons with other parts of the country;
- Effects of climate and the passage of time on buildings;
- Plants and animals in the local environment.

Music
- Local shops and traditions;
- Sounds.

3. Houses and homes

Everyone lives in a home of some kind, and this topic allows children to draw upon their own personal experiences. It is possible to set up some of the activities suggested here as school-based projects. However, it is also possible to involve parents as children gather data from their own homes and undertake practical tasks.

Considerable emphasis will be placed upon shape and pattern work, but there are also opportunities for basic calculation.

1. Where do you live? 1

Age range
Five to six.

Group size
The whole class.

What you need
A set of identical pictures of each different type of home, including semi-detached houses, detached houses, flats and so on.

What to do
Ask the children to find out the different types of homes in which the children within the class live. This should lead to an interesting discussion about classification. For example, should a flat in a three-storey block be considered the same as a flat in a multi-storey block? When you have established the different kinds of homes, create a picture graph of your findings. Ask each child in turn to put one of the pictures of her type of home in the correct column. Ask the children to count the number of pictures in the column after they have added their

picture. When every child has placed her picture in the correct column, count up the total number of pictures in each column. Label the graph correctly, and then ask the children some questions about it; for example:
- What is the most common type of home in the class?
- What is the least common type of home in the class?
- If you added together the semi-detached and detached houses, how many would you have?

Follow-up
A group of children could visit another class and gather data on housing. How similar will the results be?

2. Where do you live? 2

Age range
Five to seven.

Group size
Individuals.

What you need
A set of class name cards, pictures of the different kinds of homes that the children live in, a large piece of sugar paper, a large marker pen.

What to do
Give one child the set of name cards and the pictures of different types of home. Ask him to lay out the name cards down the left-hand side of the sugar paper and the home pictures down the right-hand side. He can then go around the rest of the class and find out what sort of homes the other children live in. Depending on the age and ability of the child, he could design his own data collection sheet and gather all the information before returning to the name and picture cards. Less confident or less able children could gather one result at a time. Finally, the child can draw a line between each name and the picture of the relevant type of home. He will then have created his own mapping diagram. If the lines are crossed, he may want to sort out the names so that all those linked to one type of home are together.

Don't forget to set a range of questions for the children to answer. The previous activity provides some examples of such questions. You might also want to ask some questions about specific children, for example, 'What kind of house does John live in?' Do more girls than boys live in flats, and if so, what does this prove?'

3. What's in a room?

Age range
Five to seven.

Group size
Small groups.

What you need
Pictures of typical rooms in a house.

What to do
Begin by asking the children to write down a list of all the objects that might appear in the different rooms of a house. They will have to decide what they will count and what they will exclude. For example, will table lamps and soft furnishings such as curtains be excluded? For

the youngest children this could be done pictorially either by drawing the items or cutting them out of magazines. The contents of the rooms could then be represented in the form of Venn diagrams, with the intersection between the sets containing the items that are common to more than one room.

Slightly older children could develop this work further by looking at the properties of different items in each room; for example, objects with four legs, free-standing objects and so on.

Follow-up
Develop design work as the children discuss and test variations in an attempt to understand why household objects are designed in a particular way. Children could also evaluate why certain rooms contain fewer items than others.

4. Room plans

Age range
Five to seven.

Group size
Two to four.

What you need
Cut-out shapes to represent different rooms and items of furniture, scrap paper.

What to do
Although young children will not have a sophisticated understanding of spatial relationships, they can begin to make plans of familiar rooms at home. The very youngest children could be given cut-out shapes to represent each of the rooms in their house. They might not be aware of the total ground floor plan of their

house, but their attempts to solve the problem could provide excellent work in sequencing and ordering. For example, 'This is my room and mummy's room is next door. The bathroom is just across the landing'. This allows children to use positional language such as 'beside', 'next to' and so on.

Older children may have a rough idea of the shapes of particular rooms, and they could cut out their own shapes and order them accordingly. This could lead to a discussion on proportion; for example, the shape cut out for the bedroom is bigger than the shape for the toilet, but not as big as the one for the living room. When the children have done this, they could then be given shapes to represent the individual items of furniture in the different rooms. Can they arrange these so that they match the layout of their living room or bedroom at home?

Follow-up
When the children have become familiar with this exercise they could represent their classroom in a similar way.

5. Carpet tiles

Age range
Five to seven.

Group size
Pairs.

What you need
Carpet tiles.

What to do
A set of carpet tiles is an excellent resource for both younger and older children (see Activity 9 on page 41). The very youngest children can count individual tiles, stepping on them as they walk, and they also provide an excellent way of introducing number bonds. For example, give two children a set of tiles and ask them to use the tiles to make 'the story of 5' — 4+1, 2+3 and so on. They are also excellent for introducing the commutative law of multiplication (that is, a×b=b×a). For example, ask the children to lay out two rows of

three tiles. They should then lay out three rows of two tiles. Children who are less familiar with multiplication facts can be given, say, ten tiles and asked to find the multiplication facts to make up that number.

Follow-up
The carpet tiles offer opportunities to explore a range of other mathematical concepts.
● Area: ask the children to measure out a particular space using square metre tiles.
● Plane shapes: what shapes can be made by putting together different numbers of carpet tiles?
● Height: ask the children to measure each other when lying down, using carpet tiles.
● Graphs: use the carpet tiles to create an enormous block graph on a theme related to houses and homes.

6. The view from above

Age range
Seven to nine.

Group size
Individuals.

What you need
Photocopiable page 116.

What to do
If the children are going to design accurate floor plans of their homes, they need to be able to draw items from a 'bird's-eye' view. Photocopiable page 116 shows a number of household objects from a bird's-eye view, which the children should try to identify. The sheet also

leaves room so that they can draw some of their own objects from this perspective and use the drawings in a floor plan of their living room or bedroom. They can also provide drawings of objects taken from other angles.

Follow-up
● Ask the children to name the different shapes they are drawing – squares, rectangles, hexagons and so on.
● Ask them to circle all the right angles they can find.

7. My room

Age range
Eight to eleven.

Group size
Individuals.

What you need
Pencils, paper.

What to do
Ask the children to make a fairly rough sketch of their own bedroom from memory. They should attempt to put items in the correct places and get the shape of the room right. Ask them also to mark in the windows and doors. They should then try to make a sensible estimate of the measurements of their room. This is very difficult to do without some guidance, so measure out the whole classroom or parts of the classroom first, and make these measurements available to the children. They can then attempt to relate the measurements of their own bedrooms to the information you have provided.

The children should carry out a more accurate measuring exercise at home to compare with their estimates and sketches. It might be worthwhile sending a letter to parents explaining the purpose of the activity and how you hope parents will assist. You could also set additional tasks for the children to do, such as finding out the perimeter of their bedrooms, or asking them how they would go about measuring the height of the walls.

When the children bring the information back to school, let them compare their estimates with the actual figures. What would they consider to be a reasonable level of error? Using their accurate measurements the children could then decide on a scale and prepare scale drawings of their bedrooms.

Follow-up
- By working out the average size and shape of the class's bedrooms the children can create the typical bedroom. What are the most common features of the children's bedrooms?
- The children could then progress to designing the ideal bedroom of the future.

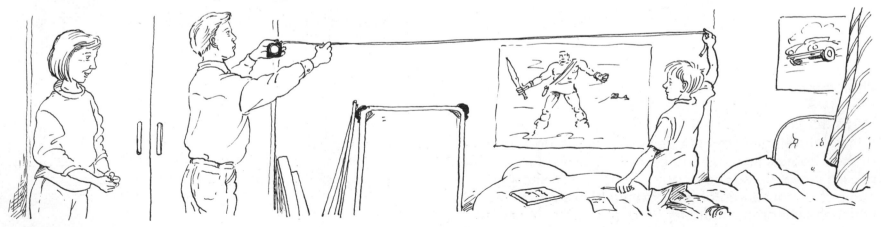

8. Bricks

Age range
Eight to ten.

Group size
Pairs.

What you need
LEGO bricks, photocopiable page 117.

What to do
Take the children outside to look at the brickwork in local houses. They should use photocopiable page 117 as a reference and recording sheet. It identifies the four main arrangements of bricks: English bond; Flemish bond; Norman herringbone; and heading bond. The children could list the addresses of local houses which are built using these styles. They could also identify other types of structure where no bricks are apparent.

When the children return to the classroom, they could use the LEGO bricks to create the brickwork patterns.

9. 100 carpet tiles

Age range
Eight to eleven.

Group size
Small groups or the whole class.

What you need
100 carpet tiles.

What to do
Buying 100 carpet tiles is an excellent investment in practical mathematical equipment. The tiles can be used to measure out the floor areas of rooms in the school by laying them out, or you can make up the measurements of imaginary rooms and ask the children to calculate how many carpet tiles would be needed to cover the floor. However, carpet tiles can be used for a whole range of other mathematical investigations, particularly if you number them consecutively from 1 to 100.

- Form the tiles into a 100 square and ask the children to stand on the 'stations' of a particular multiplication table, for example, the multiples of 2 or 6, and see what patterns are formed.
- Look at a square within the larger 100 square and ask the children to add up the numbers in that square.
- Practise multiplication tables by asking two children to race to the correct square when asked a multiplication question.
- Ask the children to find out the minimum number of squares necessary to make shapes such as kites, hexagons, octagons and so on.

Follow-up
The children could illustrate some of their findings on paper 100 squares.

10. Spirit-level and plumb-line

Age range
Ten to eleven.

Group size
Individuals or small groups.

What you need
A clear plastic bottle, water, a piece of string, a weight, a commercial spirit-level.

What to do
To begin with, ask the children to identify the places around the classroom where they can see right angles. They can then go on to make two simple tools to test whether things are horizontal or vertical.

A spirit-level can be made using a clear, straight-sided plastic bottle. Fill it up with water, but leave a small amount of air in the bottle. Lay the bottle on a surface. If a bubble of air comes up to the centre of the bottle, then the surface is level or horizontal.

Ask the children to compare this simple spirit-level with a commercial one. Can they suggest any alterations they might make to their spirit-level to make it more accurate?

A plumb-line can be made quite simply by attaching a piece of string to a weight. To test whether or not a wall is vertical, attach the line to the wall. If the line hangs straight down and parallel to the wall, then the wall is upright and vertical.

Ask the children to test the following objects to see whether or not they are horizontal or vertical:

- a table top;
- the floor;
- a sink base;
- a wall;
- a door;
- a window.

The children could then make up their own list of things they have found in the classroom which are horizontal or vertical. Do they think the spirit-level and plumb-line could help them to locate right angles?

Follow-up
Ask the children to speculate on the practical consequences of not having tools like spirit-levels and plumb-lines.

11. Buying a house

Age range
Ten to eleven.

Group size
Individuals or pairs.

What you need
Information from estate agents.

What to do
Ask a local estate agent to visit the school and describe the different elements of her work. The children can then write out a description of their own home and, if possible, measure the rooms. Failing that, use estate agents' information to calculate the total floor area of a property which is up for sale. By comparison with the prices of similar houses, the children could estimate the market value of their own home.

The children can do some work on mortgages using a calculator. If a house costs £50,000, what would a five per cent or ten per cent deposit be? They could work out how much a mortgage would cost over 20 years if there was an interest rate of ten per cent per annum. The children can take a range of salaries and see whether or not different people could afford the mortgage. Finally, they can work out what the estate agent's commission would be if she took half of one per cent of the purchase price.

Follow-up
Invite a local bank manager to discuss the different accounts and interest rates available. The children could then work out the interest due on different balances.

Classroom display ideas

- Make a three-dimensional scale model of a house based on floor plans or estate agents' information.
- Make a large-scale display of the different brick patterns found locally using art techniques such as marbling and sponging to create appropriate textures.
- Create a 'mini-room' in an area of the classroom using carpet, chairs, a chest of drawers and so on, with the measurements of each displayed.
- Using information gathered from individual children, create a large wall display to show the 'average' bedroom.
- Using carpet tiles, display some of the results of the investigations undertaken in Activities 5 and 9.
- Put a range of bird's-eye views of common household items up on the wall. Invite visitors to the classroom to guess what they are.
- Make a display of different roof shapes.
- If you have a kiln in school, allow the children to fire their own bricks (the alternative is to let them dry in the air). Prepare a list of the steps involved in making a brick.
- Design and display estate agents' information, perhaps in a class 'estate agency' with chairs, a desk, a telephone and a book of properties. The children who visit the office could come with details of a salary and the price range they are interested in. The estate agent could work out their mortgages based on a ten per cent interest rate over 20 years.

Links with other curriculum areas

PE
- Making house shapes;
- Using movement to dramatise the effect of climatic conditions such as wind.

English
- Describing the rooms in a house;
- Writing an estate agent's prospectus;
- Writing letters to different people in a household.

Art
- Making texture rubbings from house exteriors;
- Sketching interesting door and window patterns;
- Looking at interior designs such as wallpaper patterns, appropriate colour combinations etc.

Geography
- Homes in different parts of the world;
- The influence of social and economic factors on patterns of living.

Houses and homes

Music
- Making sounds associated with different rooms in the house.

Technology
- Making model houses using junk materials and construction toys;
- Designing homes for different purposes, eg for a large family or a family with pets.

Science
- Considering the different materials used to construct houses;
- Looking at the effect of forces and climate on houses;
- Looking at animal habitats.

History
- Homes through the ages – prehistoric, Roman, Tudor;
- Changes in building techniques;
- Changing styles in home decoration and the influence of advertising.

4. Journeys

The topic of journeys is an all-encompassing one. It can include journeys on the bus or train, in the car or even walking in the local neighbourhood. It can also include journeys to other areas or countries, and holidays abroad can be a rich source of mathematics with all they entail in planning and preparation. As a mathematical theme, the topic has very close links with geography as children use maps and other sources of information. However, basic mathematical skills such as adding and multiplication can be practised in real life contexts as children use holiday brochures and work out exchange rates.

1. Instructions

Age range
Five to six.

Group size
Individuals or pairs.

What you need
Card, metre sticks or tape-measures.

What to do
Prepare a set of cards which give simple instructions such as 'Choose a starting point, walk three paces forward, turn right . . .' Use simple instructions which make use of numbers, right and left orientation (for example, 'turn right', 'turn left'), and the language of direction, for example, forwards, backwards, behind and in front of.

Take the children into the hall or playground and tell them to imagine that they are explorers who have been given instructions for a journey. This idea could be elaborated into a full role-playing exercise. Each child should take his or her instruction card and follow the instructions on it, or a partner could read the instructions out. If you are working outside, the children can chalk their names by their starting and finishing points. They could then measure the distance between the two points. If there have been a lot of forwards and backwards movements, they might find that the distance between the two points is not very great.

Once the children have completed their first journey everyone can change cards and start again from where they ended up the last time. When they have carried out all the instructions again, they could see how far they have journeyed in total by measuring the direct line distance between where they started and where they ended up. Who has travelled the shortest distance?

Follow-up
The children could make up instruction cards for each other, writing on the card their estimation of the distance between the starting and finishing points.

2. Time and place

Age range
Five to seven.

Group size
Individuals.

What you need
Cards, paper, pencils, pens.

What to do
Young children's first experiences of going on a journey will be based around the neighbourhood. Make up a set of journey cards which reflect this type of journey, such as 'Walking to school', 'Going to the shops', 'Visiting Grandma' and so on. You could also ask the children to compile a list of all the journeys they make and write cards for them too. Then make up time cards which show lots of different times, such as 'Half past eight in the morning' and 'Four o'clock in the afternoon', and finally make up transport cards, such as 'Walking' and 'In the car'.

For the very youngest children it would probably be better to use picture cards instead of word cards, although they are likely still to need help with the time cards.

Mix the cards up in their three bundles and ask the children each to choose one card from the journey bundle. Then ask them to find appropriate cards in the other bundles. If they cannot find the time card they want, they could make up their own one. When they have three cards which describe their journey (what time they started it, how they went and where), they could then write a few sentences about the journey. You could also have a pile of cards for days of the week.

Follow-up
As children become more proficient in their understanding of time, you could introduce 'am' or 'pm' on the cards or use 24 hour clock times.

3. My journey to school

Age range
Six to seven.

Group size
Individuals.

What you need
Local map book (for teacher reference).

What to do
Young children should be given opportunities to describe the journey they take to school. This will largely be a verbal activity, but it will help them in the use of language and concepts of direction. You can make best use of this activity by prompting the children with questions like 'What is the name of the road you cross?' 'Do you turn right or left when you get to the other side?' Use the local map to assist you if you are not familiar with the locality.

Slightly older children might be able to represent their journey with a simple sketch plan. See how far they have identified the major features of their journey such as roads crossed and landmarks passed. This is much more important than their ability to deal with scale or perspective at this stage.

Follow-up
Make a list of all the journeys made around the school, for example, to the secretary's office, the headteacher's room, the toilet, the school field and so on. Ask the children to describe these journeys and draw simple route maps.

4. Around the town

Age range
Seven to nine.

Group size
Individuals.

What you need
Photocopiable page 118.

What to do
Journeys involve travelling a distance either on foot or by some other means of transport. Many maps indicate the distances between areas, and this activity is designed to introduce the concept of distance together with the idea of scale. Photocopiable page 118 shows a map of a small town with certain features such as a school, park and railway station marked on it. Also indicated on the map are the distances between certain points. Ask the children to try to answer some of the questions contained on the sheet. These questions are designed to test how far they understand how to calculate distances between two points on a map and how far they understand the idea of scale. You can add additional questions or additional pieces of information if you want. For example, if you provide information about walking speeds and car speeds you can ask how long it would take to cover certain distances.

Follow-up
● The idea of scale can also be reinforced by looking at toy cars and dolls and working out what scale they are designed to.
● The children could draw their own pictures or plans and calculate what the scale is, using what they know about the size of their object in real life.

5. North, east, south, west

Age range
Seven to nine.

Group size
Individuals or pairs.

What you need
Cards, pencils, a simple map with an arrow to show the north but no other compass symbols (see photocopiable page 118), a compass.

What to do
Before the children start to use a compass, they will need to be familiar with the compass points and the relationship between them. They also need to understand why compass directions are important.

Begin by asking the children why it is necessary to have compass directions. Give them a card each, and ask them to write in the four main compass points. You can help the children to understand the relative positions of the compass points by teaching them a simple rhyme such as, working clockwise, '**N**ever **E**at **S**hredded **W**heat'. With your help, the children could then put in other compass points such as north-west and south-east.

Present the children with the simple map on photocopiable page 118. Ask them to align the north on their card with north on the map. You can then set them some simple questions based on the map. For example:
- Is the roundabout east or west of the tourist centre?
- If you began at the railway station and wanted to reach the shopping centre, in what direction would you have to travel?
- What is the southernmost landmark on the map?

When the children have finished this activity, they can use a compass in the school playground to establish which way is north. They can then work out, in simple terms, the direction of other landmarks such as the town centre, the shops, the leisure centre or their house.

Follow-up
The children can create their own simple maps of the area.

6. Getting there on time

Age range
Seven to eleven.

Group size
Individuals or pairs.

What you need
A selection of bus and train timetables.

What to do
An important part of planning a journey is choosing the best means of transport and the correct times. Show the children the selection of bus and train timetables. How easy do they think the information is to read? If they do not think it is very easy because, for example, the print is too small, they could write to the bus or train company and let them know. Ask the children to plan some journeys using the timetables. They should ask themselves some of the following questions:
● What is the earliest train or bus they could catch to set out on their journey?
● What is the last train or bus they could catch to get home?
● If they want to arrive or get home before a certain time, what bus or train would they have to catch?
● Are there any days of the week or seasons of the year when it is not possible to make such a journey?
● How many times in the day could they make the journey there and back?
    You could also set the children some problems. For example, what would happen if they were delayed at a particular point on the journey?

Follow-up
Using the information gathered from the timetables, the children could put together a travel itinerary for a particular journey. They could also include any other information that might be useful, such as alternative methods of transport, cost and so on.

7. Going places

Age range
Nine to eleven.

Group size
Individuals.

What you need
Photocopiable page 119, rulers.

What to do
Photocopiable page 119 provides a distance table which shows the direct distances between towns.

The children will need to be taught how to use the table. A simple way of doing this is to give them two rulers each. They should place the first ruler vertically from a city on the horizontal axis. Then they should place the second ruler horizontally from another city on the vertical axis. Where the two rulers meet shows the direct distance between the two cities.

Once the children understand this procedure you can ask them the following questions:

• What is the distance between any two cities on the table?
• Is the distance between London and Glasgow longer than the distance between London and Edinburgh?
• What is the shortest distance between two cities on the table?

The children could also be asked to find out the time it would take to get from one city to another, travelling at different speeds. They could then prepare a table which would show the time it would take travelling between, for example, London and York, at 40mph, 50mph, 60mph and 70mph.

Follow-up
Ask the children to make a table to show the distances of four places from their home town. They might need a map book which has distances marked in it if they are going to find this out for themselves.

8. A holiday abroad

Age range
Nine to eleven.

Group size
Individuals or pairs.

What you need
Various holiday brochures, calculators.

What to do
Planning a journey abroad involves many mathematical skills, and this activity and the next two can be combined to create a larger 'topic within a topic' if you wish.

Begin by approaching a local travel agency and asking for a range of current brochures. Ask the children to look through these and identify the types of information they provide.

You could then provide some holiday requests for the children to meet. Better still, however, ask other children to come into your class travel agency and make holiday requests in respect of:
- where they want to go;
- when they want to go;
- the length of the holiday;
- the departure and destination points;
- special requests, for example, diet;
- the standard of the hotel;
- the maximum amount they are prepared to pay.

The 'travel agents' will then have a whole range of permutations to work with and a number of calculations to carry out. They need to ensure that they provide a 'bottom line' price which includes surcharges, VAT and so on. They might also want to advise their customers on value for money, so although cost is the major factor,

they need to be able to provide advice on a range of other issues. When they have reached agreement with the customer, they need to write up the various details and submit them to you for checking. They will also have to work out have a deposit.

Follow-up
Arrange a visit to a travel agency and look particularly at how the computer programmes that they use allow for a range of choices to be presented according to different criteria.

9. Foreign exchange

Age range
Nine to eleven.

Group size
Pairs.

What you need
Exchange rate tables from newspapers or banks, toy money to represent British and foreign currency.

What to do
Any journey abroad will require the correct currency. Many children will have had experience of going abroad on holiday and using foreign currency. This activity is designed to test their ability in working with exchange rates. Consult a newspaper in the morning or, better still, ask a local bank to provide information every day for a week or a fortnight to the children, who will phone them up each day from the school office. When this information is available, the children can calculate the amounts of different foreign currencies they would get in exchange for a particular number of pounds sterling. Ask the children to plot on a graph the variations in exchange rates over a week or a fortnight.

The bank may also be able to provide information from further back. The children could then create a line graph representing the rate of exchange against a number of European currencies. They could calculate the average rate over a week and come to some conclusion about which is the best currency to have from the traveller's point of view.

Why does the exchange rate fluctuate? This is something children could explore in simple terms. You could also set some additional problems. For example, before setting off on a journey, a family converted 70 per cent of their holiday money into foreign currency at a particular rate. However, at different times during the holiday, when they converted the remainder of their pounds sterling into foreign currency, the rates changed. By specifying the rate changes and the amount of money changed, you could ask the children to calculate how much foreign currency the family had in total for their holiday. Would they have been better off converting all their pounds sterling into foreign currency before starting out on their journey?

Follow-up
The children could create their own currency for a journey to an imaginary place. What would the exchange rate be? Would there be any special conditions? For example, they may decide that for the first £50 converted, there is one exchange rate, but everything above £50 is at another rate.

10. Time zones

Age range
Ten to eleven.

Group size
Individuals.

What you need
Time zone charts.

What to do
Going on a journey abroad may well involve moving into a different time zone. Using a time zone chart, the children can calculate how far ahead of or behind Greenwich Mean Time certain places are. They could also work out how many time zones they would have to pass through to visit certain places, such as Australia or New Zealand. If the children appear to have a good understanding of this, you could then ask them to work out the cumulative effects of stopping at two or three different time zones over a period of days. Do people actually 'lose' time?

You could also ask the children to consider the effects of British Summer Time and the relationship of Britain with other European time zones during that period.

Classroom display ideas

- Create a display showing the different products which might be needed on a foreign holiday. Put the price against each item and display a grand total.
- Display a set of 'instructions for journeys' cards (see Activity 1) and invite visitors to the classroom to follow the instructions.
- Make a display of directional words on a large frieze showing a journey from home to school.
- Make a montage of as many different timetables as children can find and bring into school.
- Put a large-scale directional card on the wall and, using the compass, establish north. Display a large arrow pointing in that direction.
- Draw some pictures of different areas of the school and locality and display them as being either north, east, south or west of the classroom.
- Set up a class travel agency. Put travel posters on the wall, and set up tables and chairs, telephones, pot plants and so on. Invite other children from the school to come and book their holidays.
- The children could make their own passports containing their vital personal details. These could be displayed on the wall.
- Divide the classroom into different time zones. Ask a child standing in a particular area what the time is in her zone.
- Have a large-scale display of currency rates and change them every day. This could be complimented by a weather chart showing different parts of the world, with the temperatures recorded over a period of time.

Links with other curriculum areas

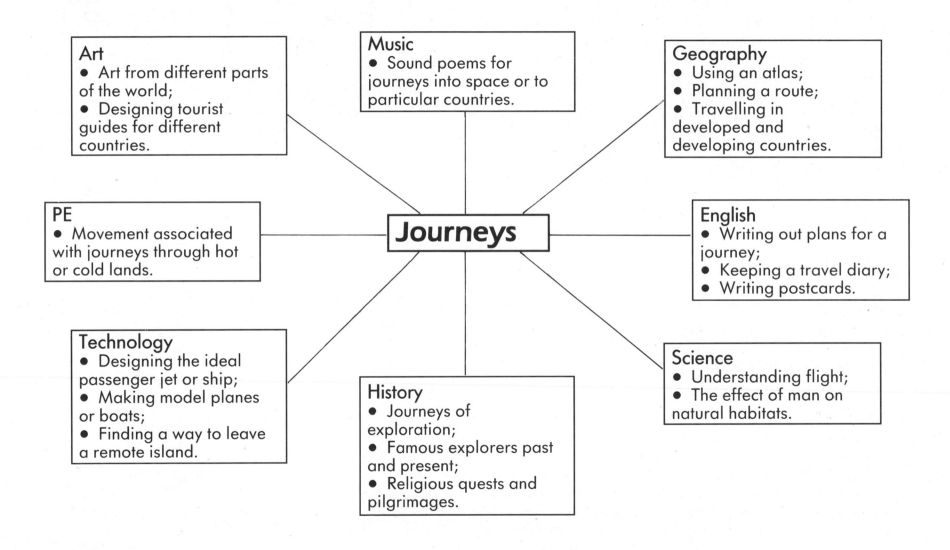

Art
- Art from different parts of the world;
- Designing tourist guides for different countries.

Music
- Sound poems for journeys into space or to particular countries.

Geography
- Using an atlas;
- Planning a route;
- Travelling in developed and developing countries.

PE
- Movement associated with journeys through hot or cold lands.

Journeys

English
- Writing out plans for a journey;
- Keeping a travel diary;
- Writing postcards.

Technology
- Designing the ideal passenger jet or ship;
- Making model planes or boats;
- Finding a way to leave a remote island.

History
- Journeys of exploration;
- Famous explorers past and present;
- Religious quests and pilgrimages.

Science
- Understanding flight;
- The effect of man on natural habitats.

5. Sport

Sport is always a popular topic for the summer months. There are often a number of sporting events happening at school at this time, usually culminating in the school sports day. Such a topic offers many practical opportunities for mathematics, with the added incentive of participation in sporting activities! The summer is also the time when many national and international sporting events are held and these never seem to fail to capture the imagination. Wimbledon, the World Cup and the Olympic Games are just three examples. Without any prompting, children will often be doing mathematics as they keep their own records of events, scores and winners. Capitalise on all this interest and undertake a topic which will make the very best use of time during the summer term.

1. Strips

Age range
Five to six.

Group size
Individuals.

What you need
Long strips of paper, colouring pencils or felt-tipped pens.

What to do
Football strips usually have interesting colours and patterns. Ask the children to find some examples in books or, better still, let them bring in examples from home. Ask them to look at the patterns and describe these in their own words. They can then copy the patterns on to the paper to make supporters' 'scarves'. These scarves can be displayed as a collage.

Finally, let the children design their own football strips, using a variety of colours and patterns. You could set them different criteria to work to, such as three colours in stripes or two colours in four squares.

Follow-up
The children could explore the number of permutations which can be achieved using only three different colours.

2. Bouncing balls

Age range
Five to seven.

Group size
Pairs.

What you need
A variety of balls such as footballs, rugby balls, tennis balls, airflow balls and so on.

What to do
Different balls bounce in different ways and this activity is designed to encourage children to explore how high different balls bounce. First, explain to the children the idea of a fair test so that they are aware that the different balls should be bounced with roughly equal force each time. Which kind of ball do they think will bounce the highest? Do smaller balls generally bounce higher than bigger balls? Is the shape of the ball a relevant factor? (In other words, do oval rugby balls bounce differently from round footballs?) Does the material the ball is made from make a difference? The children should begin to make hypotheses and form generalisations, talking and writing about their findings.

Set the children the task of actually finding out how high the balls bounce. Try not to provide too many clues to begin with. If the children are struggling, ask them to make some estimates based on their own heights.

Follow-up
● Ask the children to see if there are any relationships between how high a ball will bounce and how far it can be thrown or kicked.
● If you have any old balls, cut them up so that the children can see what is inside them. Does this provide them with any clues as to how high the ball will bounce?

3. Teams

Age range
Five to seven.

Group size
The whole class.

What you need
A large hall or playground, a range of common PE equipment such as bats and balls.

What to do
Take all the children into the playground and space them out around the area. Tell them that you are going to call a number and that you want the children to form groups of that size. Use numbers that the children are working on in class at the time. It is likely that you will have remainders, so ask the children left over to form a group and tell you how many are in it. When they are in their groups, tell the children to make up a game which involves all the team members. It can be a game with which the children are already familiar, or it can be a brand-new game. After the children have been playing their games for a while, you can shout out new instructions. The children should then make up a new game involving all the children in the new group.

   Encourage the children to think of sports or games which can be played with the number of children in the group at any one time; for example, if there are two children in the group, they could use the bats and balls to play a kind of tennis. This activity is an excellent way of familiarising children with numbers and multiples of numbers. It also encourages them to design their own games or draw upon their knowledge of team games.

4. Spot the ball

Age range
Five to seven.

Group size
Up to four.

What you need
Hoops, a selection of different shaped and coloured balls, a large hall or playground.

What to do
Ask the children to gather together all the balls that meet one particular criterion, for example, all the yellow balls, and put these in a hoop. Then ask them to gather together all the balls that fit another criterion, for example, all the tennis balls, and put these into another hoop. There might be some balls that fall into both categories, that is, yellow tennis balls. If the children are not familiar with Venn diagrams you could ask them to suggest a way in which the yellow tennis balls could be accommodated. You can then develop this work by setting problems such as: 'Make a Venn diagram that shows all the footballs that are green and made of plastic'. See if any of the children can make a Venn diagram with four hoops.

Follow-up
Ask the children to identify their three favourite sports. Can they then draw a simple picture to illustrate these?

5. Personal fact-file

Age range
Seven to eleven.

Group size
Pairs.

What you need
Tape-measures, scales, photocopiable page 120.

What to do
Many sports provide information about what young athletes of certain ages and physical characteristics can be expected to achieve. The children can work in pairs to collect the data needed to complete photocopiable page 120. This information can then be used to check individual sporting performances against standardised tables. (Your local school sports association is likely to be able to provide these for you.)

However, before the children start measuring, encourage them to make estimates of each other's measurements. It is helpful to provide them with some kind of baseline so that intelligent estimates can be made. Choose a couple of children (boys or girls) who appear to be average in each of the characteristics and work out their measurements. The children will then be better prepared to start estimating and measuring.

Follow-up
● The children can collect these statistics about themselves at the beginning of each term, so that they can chart their growth over a longer period of time. By how much have they grown or put on weight? What is the percentage increase?
● Ask the children to work out class averages for each of the attributes. What differences are there between male and female averages? How many children are below average? Finally, who are 'Mr and Miss Average' in the class – the two children who come nearest the class average on the greatest number of attributes?

6. Create a game

Age range
Seven to eleven.

Group size
Up to four.

What you need
Graph paper for planning the activity, a large hall or playground.

What to do
Ask the children to plan and design their own outdoor game. You can present this as a completely open task, but in order to derive mathematical benefit from it, it is better to establish some simple ground rules. Specify some basic principles of the game, for example, it has to be a ball game, it has to involve four people and it has to have three simple rules. The children can then use the graph paper to plan out the playing area – you might want this to be based on a scale drawing of your actual playing area. The children could then create a decision tree to illustrate the basic rules of the game.

Finally, they should go outside and try out their game. How simple are the rules to follow? How frequently are the participants involved? Could a spectator understand and participate in the game after watching for a short time?

Follow-up
● The children could design games for larger numbers of people. Is this easier or harder than designing a game for four players?
● Ask the children to try designing board games, starting off by setting out the board as a grid square and using coordinates to plot the activities in each of the individual squares. You might want to insist that every game has some kind of mathematical activity built into it, for example, mental addition and subtraction or multiplication tables.

7. Fields and pitches

Age range
Eight to nine.

Group size
Individuals.

What you need
Photocopiable page 121, reference books on sport.

What to do
Almost all field sports and games require some kind of ground markings. The children can use photocopiable page 121 and the reference books to investigate the different ground markings needed for a range of sports and games. Set them the following questions:
* What shapes can you see?
* How many right angles are there?
* Can you find any relationship between the size of the pitches and fields investigated, and the number of players?
* Using the actual dimensions of the fields and pitches, can you find the areas of each of them?
* Can you prepare scale drawings of each of the fields or pitches?

Follow-up
* Using a sport or game with which they are familiar, the children could investigate how many lines they could remove without affecting the rules of the sport or game.
* The children could completely redesign the pitch markings of a familiar sport or game.
* Ask the children to design some ground markings for their favourite playground game.

8. The school sports day

Age range
Eight to eleven.

Group size
Any.

What you need
Pencils, paper, calculators, stop-watches.

What to do
School sports days are a feature of every primary school's life, and by involving the children at every stage, you will be offering them many mathematical opportunities. As soon as you know the planned date for the sports day, set the children to work planning a timetable for practice events and heats. They will need to know how many events each class or year group will be having and how much practice time they need. The children can also start planning the layout of the school field – they will need graph paper to do a scale drawing. They will have to predict the number of parents and guests likely to come and the amount of space they will take up. If programmes are to be printed, the children could talk to the school secretary in order to cost this out. Perhaps there could be a charge for the programmes, in which case the children could work out income against expenditure. If they know the number of seats likely to be needed, they could work out various seating arrangements using rows and columns.

On the day itself, the children could be responsible for keeping a record of the number of people who attend. They could also:

● act as timekeepers for all the field and track events;
● keep running totals of individual and team scores;
● act as adjudicators on field events such as the high jump and long jump;
● ensure that the correct apparatus is in place for each event.

9. At the races

Age range
Nine to eleven.

Group size
Two to four.

What you need
A range of measuring equipment, for example, tape-measures, stop-watches and so on.

What to do
In almost all the indoor and outdoor sports that children participate in, they should be able to measure their own performance. Before allowing them to do so, however, it is important for them to consider the need for accuracy in such measurements. Is the same level of accuracy needed when measuring the time taken to run 100 metres and the distance covered by a ball thrown in the cricket ball 'shot-put'? If not, why not? Ask the children to set a tolerance limit for each event and consider the principles involved. For example, when measuring performance in a sprint they might want to know the time taken to the nearest hundredth of a second, whereas in the long distance race, they might only be interested in the time to the nearest minute.

Don't make it too easy for the children by telling them how to measure for each individual event and what equipment to use. Make this one of their tasks. They will also have to decide how they are going to deploy themselves; for example, in a sprint they might need one starter, two people on the finishing line and a timekeeper to ensure accuracy. They could also consider the equipment and the people necessary to score the following events:
* 100 metre sprint;
* 400 metre run;
* long jump;
* high jump;
* cricket ball shot-put.

In addition, ask the children to consider the scoring and measuring arrangements needed for all the indoor sports they play.

Follow-up
When the children have set up their scoring and recording arrangements, they need to start collecting data from the performances of their classmates. They need to ensure that their figures are accurate so that they can be transferred to a computer database. When that has been done, the data can be examined and presented in a whole range of ways; for example, pie charts and block graphs.

10. The tournament

Age range
Ten to eleven.

Group size
Individuals.

What you need
Pencils, paper.

What to do
If you have a football, netball, hockey or other team-sport tournament coming up in school, involve the children in all the preparations. Let them collect the names of all the children participating. How many teams should there be, and of what size? By what criteria would this be established? For example, is there any mathematical way of calculating the optimum size of pitch for the number of children on it at any one time?

Having decided the number of teams participating, it is necessary to work out a fixture list. The size of this will depend on the length of the tournament, but it is worth assuming that each team will play every other team at least once. Obviously, the more teams, the more complicated it is to work out a pattern or sequence of games. Here is one way of ensuring that all the possible permutations are covered with six teams.

A v B	B v C	C v D	D v E	E v F
A v C	B v D	C v E	D v F	
A v D	B v E	C v F		
A v E	B v F			
A v F				

But what about the order in which the matches are played? It is extremely unlikely that team A would play five games in a row. Can the children guess how an organisation like the Football League works out a very complicated programme of fixtures? They could perhaps write and find out.

If a small one-day tournament is taking place, the children could work out a programme of matches. This would involve both accurate timing and estimating, as each game would have to last for a set period, although the interval time between games could vary. The children would also have to take into account the length of the school afternoon and allow time for changing and clearing up.

Follow-up
Activity 11 provides the logical follow-up.

11. The big match

Age range
Ten to eleven.

Group size
Two to four.

What you need
Pencils, paper, clipboards, stop-watches.

What to do
Older children often go to watch football or netball matches involving the school team, and these occasions can be used for a range of mathematical activities. Before the game, give the children an estimation sheet to fill in, with questions such as: 'How many goals do you think will be scored today?' This will involve them in careful thought, using the data available and information based on previous experience.

During the game the children can be involved in a number of activities, from timing using stop-watches to gathering statistical data such as who has scored the goals. An interesting experiment is to follow the progress of one player during a game, keeping a record of passes made and of shots at goal.

If you have arranged a tournament like the one described in Activity 10, then there are even more possibilities for mathematical activities. For example, keep a master league table to be completed and followed by the children. This will prove an endless source of fascination as they work out how many points each team has, or what the current goal difference is for teams tying at the top. When the trophies and medals have been presented, the statistical post-mortem can begin. Here are some problems to set the children:
* How many goals were scored over the whole tournament?
* What was the average number of goals per game?
* Who was the top scorer?

However, you might want to set some open-ended questions such as the following:
* What comparisons can be drawn between the team that does best and the team that does worst in the tournament? (The age, height and weight of players could all be compared.)
* How can footballing ability be measured?
* Do goals tend to be scored in one part of the game rather than another? If so, why?

Follow-up
Ask the children to collect statistics over a number of games and see what patterns emerge. Their information could be presented graphically, for example, as a pie chart showing how one player's time has been used in a match or a frequency diagram showing the top scorers.

Classroom display ideas

- Display a fact-file about 'Mr and Miss Average' in the class.
- Set aside an area of the room to gather personal statistics from visitors to the class. Have available a height chart, some scales and a tape-measure.
- Display a block graph to show the children's favourite sports.
- Create a display of football strips, either real or drawn, highlighting the dominant shapes such as squares, triangles and rectangles.
- Display a programme of matches or a fixture list designed by the children.
- Have a collection of balls in the classroom, with labels to show their circumference, weight and texture and how high they bounce when dropped from the same height.
- Make a display of a range of different pitches, highlighting all the different shapes on them.
- Have a dartboard hanging up in a safe place, and display some problems beside it for children and visitors to solve; for example, 'Score 100 with three darts' or 'Score 50 using doubles only'.

Links with other curriculum areas

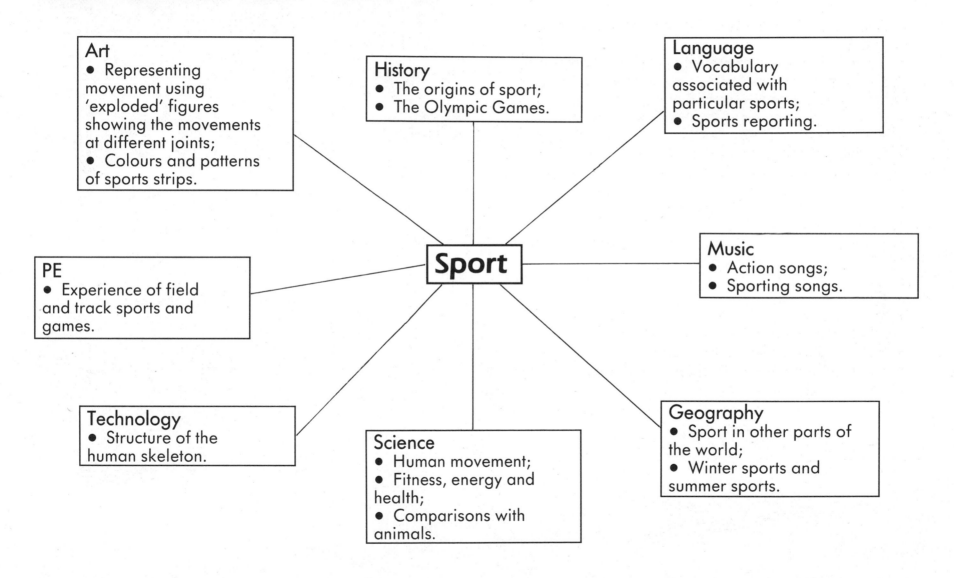

Art
- Representing movement using 'exploded' figures showing the movements at different joints;
- Colours and patterns of sports strips.

History
- The origins of sport;
- The Olympic Games.

Language
- Vocabulary associated with particular sports;
- Sports reporting.

PE
- Experience of field and track sports and games.

Sport

Music
- Action songs;
- Sporting songs.

Technology
- Structure of the human skeleton.

Science
- Human movement;
- Fitness, energy and health;
- Comparisons with animals.

Geography
- Sport in other parts of the world;
- Winter sports and summer sports.

6. Time

Of all the topics in this book, time has the most direct mathematical connections. However, as a cross-curricular topic it has links with science, technology, history, geography, art and music. The activities here are less concerned with teaching children how to tell the time than with ways of extending mathematical experience.

1. Picture time

Age range
Five to six.

Group size
Individuals or pairs.

What you need
Photocopiable page 122.

What to do
Children's first understanding of time comes from sequencing different events in the day. Begin by asking the children to recount, in the correct order, all the things they have done since getting up in the morning. They can then attempt to describe all the things that happened to them the day before. Encourage the children to use times like 'twelve o'clock' or 'half past five'. Even if they don't quite understand these phrases, they will become familiar with them. Then give the children photocopiable page 122. They should cut out all the pictures and put them in the correct order. They could talk or write about what they see, and then suggest a time for each picture.

Finally, the children could draw some pictures of their own to show things that they might do during the day, and include them in the sequence.

Follow-up
If children have already begun to tell the time, you could add some times to the pictures so that a connection can be made between what happens and when it happens.

2. Beat the clock

Age range
Five to seven.

Group size
Individuals or pairs.

What you need
A sand timer or stop-watch.

What to do
Tell the children that you are going to give them a set task to complete in a fixed period of time, for example, one minute. The task could be to build a structure using LEGO, to read a certain number of pages in a book, or to complete a particular physical activity. Ideally, the children should be able to see how the time is passing as they try to complete the task, so a sand timer would be useful.

See how far the children can complete the task in the time allowed. If they are unable to do it in the allotted time, ask them to try again. If they do it within the time, could they do the activity more slowly, but still stay within the time?

Ask the children to suggest some other activities which they could undertake within the time. They will have to make some estimates of what they can reasonably do.

Follow-up
The length of time could be extended, or the children could be asked to estimate how long the activity would take if another person was involved. Do they think it automatically follows that two people doing an activity would take half the time?

3. Picture books

Age range
Five to seven.

Group size
Individuals.

What you need
Picture books with a time theme, such as *Good Night, Good Night* by Sandra Boynton (Methuen); *The Bad-Tempered Ladybird* by Eric Carle (Picture Puffin); *The Very Hungry Caterpillar* by Eric Carle (Picture Puffin); *Just a Minute* by Anita Harper and Susan Hellard (Picture Puffin); *Mr Wolf's Week* by Colin Hawkins (Armada Picture Lions); *Clocks and More Clocks* by Pat Hutchins (Picture Puffin); *What's the Time, Rory Wolf?* by

Gillian McClure (André Deutsch); *Rhymes Around the Day* by Jan Ormerod (Picture Puffin); *Early Morning in the Barn* by Nancy Tafuri (Picture Puffin); *Hurry Up, Jessie!* by Harriet Ziefert and Mavis Smith (Simon and Schuster).

What to do

Using picture books that have a time theme has the dual advantage of teaching important concepts while also introducing a range of high-quality books.

Practise naming the days of the week using *Mr Wolf's Week*. This describes the different clothes Mr Wolf puts on each day. The children could make replicas of his clothes for each day and dress him appropriately, ensuring that the names of the days are in the correct order.

In *The Very Hungry Caterpillar*, the hero eats his way through different foods each day. The children could sequence the days according to the food eaten.

A book such as *Rhymes Around the Day* is useful because the rhymes which describe happenings at different times in the day help with sequencing. *What's the Time, Rory Wolf?* can also be used for this. Ask the children to describe the wolf's day. What does he do when he gets up? When does he go into the town?

Some books concentrate on specific times of the day, for example, *Early Morning in the Barn* and *Good Night, Good Night*.

The duration of time is covered in books like *Just a Minute* and *Hurry up, Jessie!* These reinforce figures of speech with which children will be familiar.

Once the children can tell the time, use *The Bad-Tempered Ladybird*. There is a clock face on each page and as the story develops, the children move their own clocks on to the correct time. All sorts of questions can arise. For example, it is ten o'clock. What time was it an hour ago when the ladybird met the sparrow?

Finally, older children will enjoy *Clocks and More Clocks*. This book introduces the idea of a minute in terms of both the passage of time and the distance travelled by the hands on a clock face.

Follow-up

Other books associated with time include *All in a Day* by M. Anno (Hamish Hamilton); *A Dark, Dark Tale* by R. Brown (Anderson Press); *Demon Daisy's Dreadful Week* by P. Gilli (Picture Knight); *In the Night* by J. Shipton (Collins).

4. Photo time line

Age range
Five to seven.

Group size
Individuals or pairs.

What you need
A collection of photographs on a particular theme, such as photographs of the children at different stages in their life or photographs of cars through time.

What to do
Children can learn about sequencing through studying photographs or artefacts which cover a period of years. Family photographs are ideal for this purpose as they present a very familiar subject. The children can begin by putting the photographs in the correct order. When they have done that, they can be helped to put the correct year beside each photograph. This can lead to very simple work in subtraction, for example, 'That photograph shows you at two years of age; you are six now and this is 1991, so in what year was the photograph taken?' With photographs which span a longer period of time, ask the children to put them into the correct sequence. What clues will they use? Can they describe what makes something look 'newer'?

Follow-up
The children could group together all the photographs from a particular year. They might also find other things from that year, such as newspapers, stamps, and so on.

5. The calendar

Age range
Five to seven.

Group size
Individuals or pairs.

What you need
Photocopiable page 123.

What to do
Children need to know the days of the week and the months of the year. The former can be reinforced every day at school, particularly if the week has its own routines with, for example, PE on Monday and swimming on Thursday. The children could think of something special they do each day, such as visit their

grandparents, go to ballet lessons or play football.

The months of the year are slightly more difficult to do. Begin by making a large chart on the wall or on the blackboard listing all the months of the year. The children could start off by simply putting their birthdays in. They could then add special events like Christmas or Valentine's Day. Give the children photocopiable page 123 which shows pictures of the months of the year. Jumble all the pictures together and see whether the children can put them in the correct order.

Follow-up
To develop this into a matching exercise, ask the children to cut the month labels from the bottom of the pictures and mix them all together. Can they sort the labels and pictures and put the months of the year in the correct order?

6. Just a minute

Age range
Seven to nine.

Group size
Pairs.

What you need
Stop-watches.

What to do
Children often find the passage of short periods of time very difficult to judge. To be better judges of time they need to be taught certain techniques. Begin with estimating ten seconds. Ask one child in each pair to time this on a stop-watch and the other to indicate when he or she thinks ten seconds are up. The children should then discuss how they can count a second. If they find it difficult to estimate these short periods of time, suggest that they count 'one elephant, two elephant, three elephant' or '1001, 1002, 1003', with each of these phrases taking about one second to say. Can the children find something better?

Follow-up
The children could list the occasions when it is important to be able to estimate a short period of time. They could then go on to estimate longer periods of time such as 20 seconds, 30 seconds or one minute.

7. Clocks, clocks, clocks

Age range
Seven to nine.

Group size
Individuals.

What you need
A variety of clock faces, for example, with digital displays, with Roman numerals, without numbers, with four numbers, 'backwards' clocks and so on.

What to do
Clock faces come in many different shapes and sizes and children need to be able to tell the time from whatever type of display they see. The children could begin by making a list or drawing all the different clock faces there are within the class or the school. Some of these will have cartoon characters on them, but the point here is to look for different ways of displaying the numbers. How many can the children find? How would they group the clocks? Ask them to think about other clock displays they have seen. The children could then ask themselves some questions:
● What is the easiest display to read? Easiest for whom?
● What is the hardest display to read? Hardest for whom?
● Are some displays the way they are because the clock or watch has to meet a special purpose?
● Why would people want to wear a watch which appears difficult to read?

Follow-up
Ask the children to design the ideal clock for their own use. What information would it give? How would the numerals be displayed, if they are displayed at all?

8. TV times

Age range
Nine to eleven.

Group size
Individuals.

What you need
The television page from a newspaper or a television listings magazine.

What to do
Children need opportunities to practise calculations based on times. This goes beyond merely telling the time. Television pages from newspapers or listings magazines are excellent in this respect because they provide start and finish times without actually stating how long programmes last. You can ask the children a whole range of questions based on these listings:

- Does programme X last longer than programme Y?
- What is the longest programme on BBC1 on a Tuesday?
- What is the total amount of time devoted to news on Channel 4 on a Thursday?
- How long does programme Z last?
- How long does schools television last in a week?
- What is the earliest programme on any channel?
- How much time does ITV devote to sport in a week? Is that more or less than the time devoted to news?

Follow-up
The children could take a day's programmes and classify them under some general headings, such as sport, news, comedy, drama and so on. Could they work out the relative proportions of each and present their findings in a pie chart?

9. My week

Age range
Nine to eleven.

Group size
Individuals.

What you need
A sheet to record the different activities undertaken by the children during a week.

What to do
Children are often interested in keeping diaries, and this enthusiasm can also be channelled into mathematical activities. It is important not to expect the children to keep diaries for too long, because enthusiasm usually wears off; a week is about right. Initially, the children need to decide how they are going to collect the information. Will it be a 'minute by minute' description or will information be gathered under broad headings such as 'sleeping', 'at school', 'watching TV' and so on? The latter is probably easier to manage. When the week is up, the children need to decide how they will present the information. They will have to consider issues such as the number of days and hours covered, and what happens if their activities do not add up to the total number of hours in the week. Should they present their findings as numbers or percentages? If they choose the latter, how will they display them?

Finally, ask the children to draw conclusions from their findings; for example, 'Children watch 15 hours of television a week' and 'Children watch too much television each week'. What is the difference between these conclusions? When does a mathematical finding become a moral judgement?

Follow-up
If the individual results were fed into a database, it would be possible to draw some conclusions about the activity patterns of the class as a whole.

10. A time line for the school

Age range
Nine to eleven.

Group size
Up to four.

What you need
Log books, registers and other artefacts associated with the history of the school.

What to do
Many older children in primary schools study the history of the school. This can incorporate a mathematical aspect if the children have access to a range of documents and other information from which they can compile statistics. Here are some of the questions which could be asked:

- How many children were on the school roll when it opened?
- Draw a graph representing the number of children on the school roll every five years since it opened (the frequency will depend on how old the school is).
- List three important events that happened in the school ten years ago.
- In school year X, who was the youngest child in each class?
- What proportion of the pupils were boys in school year Y?

Follow-up
The children could prepare a fact-sheet entitled 'Some interesting statistics about our school since it was opened'.

Classroom display ideas

- Make a display of all the different timepieces you can find. The local museum may be able to help.
- The children can display a sequence of pictures, with times, outlining the major happenings during their day.
- Display the days of the week and months of the year prominently around the room. Have some way of displaying the correct day, date and month.
- Make a display of all the picture books associated with time. Large friezes could be made of *The Bad-Tempered Ladybird* or *The Very Hungry Caterpillar*.
- Make a time line showing the years since the children were born. Display photographs, newspapers and artefacts from each of these years. Have a table of undated items. Can visitors decide where they belong on the time line?
- Make a display of all the things children can do in ten seconds, thirty seconds, one minute or five minutes. Leave a timer on a table along with a list of tasks for the children to undertake in these times.
- Display a pie chart showing the class's favourite television programmes over the past week.
- Display a large pie chart or graph which illustrates 'Our week' (the activities of the class as a whole, broken down into general headings such as sleeping, at school and so on).

Links with other curriculum areas

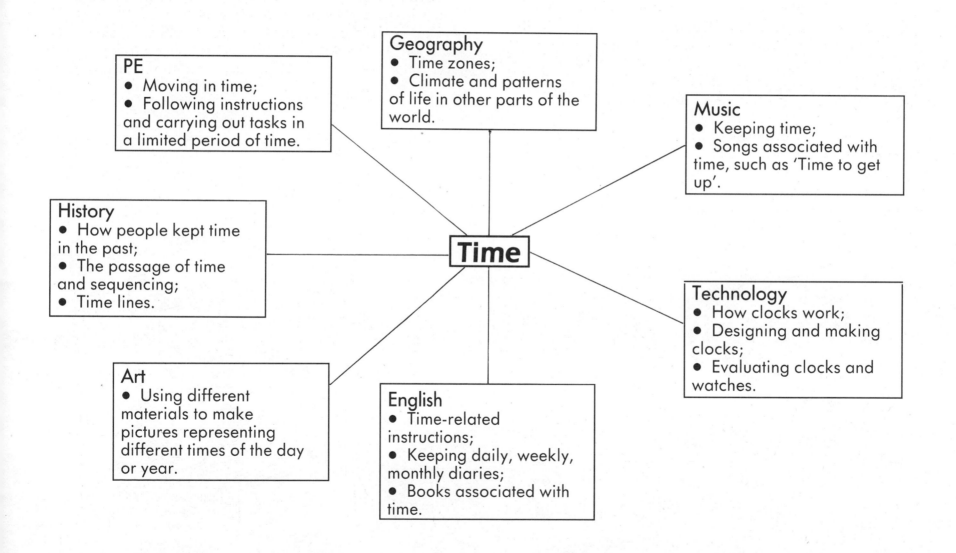

PE
- Moving in time;
- Following instructions and carrying out tasks in a limited period of time.

Geography
- Time zones;
- Climate and patterns of life in other parts of the world.

Music
- Keeping time;
- Songs associated with time, such as 'Time to get up'.

History
- How people kept time in the past;
- The passage of time and sequencing;
- Time lines.

Time

Technology
- How clocks work;
- Designing and making clocks;
- Evaluating clocks and watches.

Art
- Using different materials to make pictures representing different times of the day or year.

English
- Time-related instructions;
- Keeping daily, weekly, monthly diaries;
- Books associated with time.

7. Christmas

Christmas is always a busy time in school with the hectic round of seasonal events, assemblies, trips out, performances and parties. Additionally, there are Christmas cards and decorations to be made. Christmas as a theme offers many interesting mathematical possibilities which can easily be overlooked in the great bustle of December.

The advantages of mathematical activities based on a Christmas theme is that while they are educationally worthwhile they are also likely to hold the children's attention even though there are many other distractions. Don't forget all the other mathematical possibilities that present themselves at such a time, such as measuring and cutting card to shape, weighing ingredients or planning the school assembly.

1. Who got what?

Age range
Five to six.

Group size
Individuals.

What you need
Family name cards such as 'Dad', 'Mum', 'Ben aged 10', 'Grandma' and so on; present labels in words or pictures, such as 'aftershave', 'rollerboots', 'socks' and so on; pieces of string, Blu-Tack.

What to do
Let the children see all the family names, and the ages of the children mentioned. Begin by discussing with them the sorts of things each member of the family might receive as Christmas presents. The children should then look at the present tags and match one with each name tag by attaching a piece of string to the relevant cards with the Blu-Tack. It is worth making the point to the children that some presents might be suitable for more than one person. For example, both Dad and Colin, who is 15, could have received the aftershave. You might, however, want to ensure that there is a more specific match of one present to one person, since the children will have to reason out which present belongs to which person if there is more than one possible choice.

Use this activity to look at gender stereotyping. Do the children automatically assume that the football will go to Brian, aged ten, rather than Laura, aged eight?

Follow-up
The children could write or describe a set of criteria for choosing a present for each person. For example, Dad could be described as wanting something associated with sport, but not cricket or football. They could then give the criteria list to a friend who could choose an appropriate present.

2. Little boxes

Age range
Five to seven.

Group size
Individuals.

What you need
A selection of gift boxes, pictures of such boxes from catalogues.

What to do
All sorts of special packages appear at Christmas time. But what sorts of shapes are these gift boxes? Depending on the knowledge and experience of the children you might want to provide a pictorial identification chart of the most common three-dimensional shapes. These would include cube, cuboid, cylinder, square pyramid, triangular pyramid and so on. Alternatively, you could provide a list of characteristics of the various shapes; for example, a cube has six square faces. Once you have drawn up your chart you should allow the children to use it to identify the shapes.

You can extend this activity by asking the children to describe the different features of each shape they find. They could include, for example, the number of right angles, the number of faces, the number of edges and so on. Also, are they able to find any three-dimensional shapes that they have not seen before? How would they describe these shapes or find out what they are called?

Follow-up
Cuboids come in many different styles. If you can make up a collection of cuboids, see whether the children are able to identify them as all being the same basic shape.

3. Countdown to Christmas

Age range
Five to seven.

Group size
Individuals or the whole class.

What you need
An Advent calendar, number cards 1 to 25, charts labelled 'Number of days to Christmas Day'.

What to do
No classroom is complete at Christmas without an Advent calendar, and the children will love to gather round it each morning as one member of the class opens a window. This daily event can be extended so that it also provides a simple and enjoyable mathematical activity.

When the children open a window, ask them how many days are left until it is Christmas Day. Depending on their age and ability different children will approach this in different ways; for example, some children will want to know whether to include the day that they are in and Christmas Day itself. Discuss this and other conventions with the children; for example, we might say on a Thursday, 'There's one more day to the weekend'. What happens if the more able children subtract the current date from 24 or 25? Will that give them the number of days to Christmas?

Ask the children each day to keep a record on their personal charts of the number of days to Christmas. Don't forget to ask the youngest children how many days it will be to Christmas tomorrow or how many days it was to Christmas yesterday.

Follow-up
Ask the children to consider how many Tuesdays or Wednesdays there are until Christmas Day. Should they include Christmas Day itself if it falls on a Tuesday or Wednesday? The children should try to justify their decisions.

4. Selection boxes

Age range
Seven to ten.

Group size
Individuals or pairs.

What you need
A selection box of chocolate bars, scales, individual prices of items contained in the selection box.

What to do
Prepacked selection boxes containing different types of bars of chocolate are always extremely popular at Christmas time. But do they represent good value for money? Ask the children to investigate and find out for themselves. Don't give them too many clues to begin with. Set the problem in very general terms and see whether they can devise their own strategy.

Firstly, the children will need to know the price of the selection box. They could then weigh all the individual items in it and weigh the packaging. They will also need to add up the prices of all the items if they were to be bought individually. The children can then work out the difference between the items if bought in the selection box and if bought individually. What does that difference represent? The more able children could work this out as a percentage.

You could also ask the children to share out the additional costs of the selection box (such as packaging) among the individual items, perhaps by dividing the difference in price by the number of items in the selection box. What then does a bar of chocolate in a selection box cost? The children could also look at the packaging of the selection box and work out the cost per gram of packaging.

Finally, pose the question, 'Is it ever worth buying a selection box?' Here you will engage children in a discussion about choices based on criteria other than pure mathematical facts. Is there an acceptable level of 'on-costs', or costs over and above the cost of each individual item, for having something packaged up in a special way for Christmas? When does the cost become 'unacceptable'?

Follow-up
The children could present their findings in an attractive format. This would include a statement of the problem, a summary of the main findings in both numbers and words and some conclusions and recommendations. Perhaps all of this could be sent off to the manufacturer of the selection box!

5. Stars and 'arithmestars'

Age range
Seven to eleven.

Group size
Individuals.

What you need
Photocopiable page 124.

What to do
Stars are a popular symbol of Christmas. Ask the children to find as many stars as they can, either in books or in objects such as Christmas decorations. Ask them to identify the major features of each of the stars they find, for example, the number of points or the number of sides. Ask them to look at the shapes which make up the stars, such as triangles and pentagons.

The children can then look at the two 'arithmestars' on photocopiable page 124. In each of these 'arithmestars' all the lines must be filled in so that they add up to the same total. The children need to find out what that total is and then find the correct numbers to fill in the spaces. They will have to reason carefully to work this out.

Follow-up
Can the children design their own 'arithmestars'?

6. Costing the Christmas tree

Age range
Eight to ten.

Group size
Individuals or pairs.

What you need
Prices of real and artificial Christmas trees, calculators.

What to do
Ask the children to consider the problem of whether to buy a real or artificial Christmas tree. One way of looking at this problem is simply in terms of cost. Begin by asking the children how they would work out the relative values, and what constitutes a reasonable comparison. They will need to ensure that they compare similar sized trees to begin with, so if they have the opportunity to gather the prices themselves, make sure that they obtain proper comparative prices. Do the children automatically assume that the real tree is better value because it costs less? If not, can they work out how many years' worth of real trees they would get for

an artificial one? At what point does the artificial tree start paying for itself? If it is after five years, the children need to consider what the artificial tree would look like at that point. Would it be well worn and in need of replacement anyway?

Finally, you might ask how far cost actually influences whether or not to buy an artificial tree. Is it an important factor? What other factors are likely to be considered by someone making such a decision?

Follow-up
With more able children, you could discuss the idea of price rises or inflation. How will this affect their initial calculation? If the price rise is ten per cent a year, what will the cost of the tree be in five years? How does inflation affect the cost of the artificial tree?

7. Gift wrapping

Age range
Eight to eleven.

Group size
Individuals or pairs.

What you need
A range of different boxes, Christmas wrapping paper, sticky tape, scissors.

What to do
Set the children the task of wrapping the different boxes with the minimum amount of wrapping paper. The children need to agree on what constitutes 'wrapping' the box as opposed to just sticking enough paper on it to cover it. When that has been agreed, ask the children to choose and wrap a box. They should then write down the instructions for wrapping the box and see if someone else can follow them.

When they have wrapped the box, ask the children how they are going to compare the different sizes of paper. They will need to find the area of the paper, but this could prove difficult if the paper is not a regular shape. The children can then examine the most successful and the least successful methods of wrapping a box. Is there any pattern? For example, are there fewer folds, or are the folds smaller in the most efficient methods than in the less efficient ones? Finally, can they devise instructions for the most efficient use of wrapping paper?

Follow-up
Encourage children to make a judgment about how much of the packaging used at Christmas is necessary. What are the implications of having unnecessary packaging?

8. Santa's grotto

Age range
Eight to eleven.

Group size
Individuals or pairs.

What you need
Stop-watch, calculator.

What to do
A 'Santa's grotto' is a common feature of many shops at Christmas, and this activity will require the children to work out some facts and figures about Santa and his grotto. If you have the chance to visit a shop beforehand and do some research, so much the better. However, the children could also write to a store manager to get some information.

The children should try to calculate how many children are likely to visit Santa on an average day. They will need to know the shop's opening and closing times and how many breaks Santa takes during the day. Then they will have to calculate how long it takes Santa to see each child. This will tell them the maximum number of children Santa could see each day. However, is this likely to be the actual number each day? What about a Saturday, which will probably be much busier than a week day? Would Santa therefore have to give each child less time on a Saturday? Once the children have calculated an average daily number of children who will visit Santa, they can then work out the total number of children who will see Santa over the Christmas period. They could also work out how much money the store will make!

Follow-up
Could the children predict the factors that would affect the number of children who visit Santa? For example, what effect will the weather have, or the amount of money people have to spend?

9. The Christmas present list

Age range
Nine to eleven.

Group size
Individuals or pairs.

What you need
Catalogues with illustrations and prices of a range of Christmas goods.

What to do
Christmas is a time for choosing presents, but who gets what and how much will it cost? Ask the children to begin this activity by inventing their own family of four people. It needn't necessarily be a mum, dad and two children; it can be any type of family group. It would be best, however, if it contained at least one adult. The children should then write simple biographies for each of the members of their invented family group. These should specify age, occupation, hobbies and interests, favourite television programmes and any other information the children wish. Give the children a Christmas present budget which has to be used to buy presents for the whole family. Do not say how the budget has to be distributed, that is part of the exercise. The children can then use the catalogues to choose presents for all the family. They must work out how much each item will cost, but they must be careful not to exceed the budget you have given them.

Once the children have completed this they can compare their results. How do they justify the relative amounts given to each member of the family group? Is any one person more deserving than others? Overall, would they think that the total budget was adequate for the four people concerned? If not, what would be a realistic increase?

Follow-up
If the children have a reasonable idea of what they are going to get for Christmas, you could work out the total class expenditure on Christmas presents. This has to be done with sensitivity, though, if some children are unlikely to get as much as others.

10. Getting the hall ready

Age range
Nine to eleven.

Group size
Individuals or pairs.

What you need
Tape-measures.

What to do
The performance of the Christmas concert or play always fills the school hall with spectators. But just how many people can come and watch the performance, and how will they be accommodated? Working in pairs, the children should attempt to solve this problem.

The children will probably need to begin by working out the dimensions of the hall. They should also draw a rough plan of the area and identify any areas which will be unsuitable for seating. The children also need to check with the headteacher or whoever is in charge of the performance to find out how much space will be needed by the children in the school, both for performing and for watching. They will then be left with the total amount of space in the hall available for seating. However, you will have to remind them of the need to accommodate aisles, areas for prams and so on. They can then measure the width of a chair and calculate how many chairs they could get into the hall. How accurate does this figure need to be? Must it be exact or will figures to the nearest ten do?

When the children have done this they should provide a sketch plan of how they wish the hall to be organised. This need not be to scale as long as it supplies enough detail on which to base the seating plan. Compare the different answers that are provided.

Follow-up
The children could find out how many parents and friends are likely to attend the performances. They could work out how many performances will be needed and how many people they estimate will be at each one.

Classroom display ideas

- Make a large-scale picture of Santa with a sack full of presents for a family within a budget of £50 or £100.
- Make a block graph of the children's choices for Christmas and, if possible, compare it with the national 'Top 10' Christmas presents, which is often announced on the television news and published in the newspapers shortly before Christmas.
- Draw, paint and cut out family characters and make a list of the presents they want and the presents they have purchased for each other.
- Make a display of all the different sizes and shapes of wrapping paper the children used to wrap a box.
- Put a piece of Christmas wrapping paper on the wall and identify all the different two-dimensional shapes which can be seen on it. These can then be cut out and labelled, and displayed alongside the original sheet of wrapping paper.
- Make two displays comparing the cost of buying a chocolate selection box with the cost of buying the bars of chocolate separately.
- Bring some miniature Christmas trees into the classroom and decorate each one with a different shape, for example one tree with cubes and cuboids, another with stars and so on.
- Hang from the ceiling some of the children's 'arithmestars' (see Activity 5).
- Put up some of the plans the children have devised for seating parents in the hall for the school concert.

Links with other curriculum areas

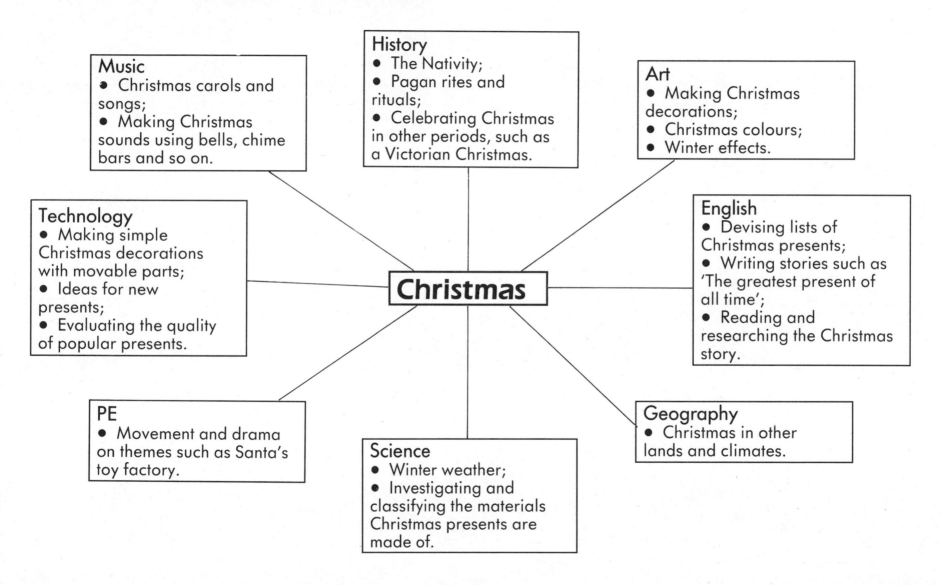

Music
- Christmas carols and songs;
- Making Christmas sounds using bells, chime bars and so on.

History
- The Nativity;
- Pagan rites and rituals;
- Celebrating Christmas in other periods, such as a Victorian Christmas.

Art
- Making Christmas decorations;
- Christmas colours;
- Winter effects.

Technology
- Making simple Christmas decorations with movable parts;
- Ideas for new presents;
- Evaluating the quality of popular presents.

Christmas

English
- Devising lists of Christmas presents;
- Writing stories such as 'The greatest present of all time';
- Reading and researching the Christmas story.

PE
- Movement and drama on themes such as Santa's toy factory.

Science
- Winter weather;
- Investigating and classifying the materials Christmas presents are made of.

Geography
- Christmas in other lands and climates.

8. Food

Food is an excellent mathematical topic because it allows many opportunities for practical work. It also enables children to make connections with local services such as restaurants, supermarkets and bakeries, and so derive mathematical work from real life situations.

Where children are working with real foodstuffs for mathematical purposes, it is important to remind them of hygiene and food safety. Food is unlikely to be suitable for consumption after mathematical investigations have been carried out!

1. Packed lunches

Age range
Five to seven.

Group size
Individuals, small groups or the whole class.

What you need
School dinner register, children's lunch boxes.

What to do
Every school day begins with the ritual of the dinner register. However, if you look closely at packed lunches, they can also offer many mathematical possibilities. Begin by asking the children to record the number of children staying for a school dinner, bringing a packed lunch or going home. This can be done by the children grouping themselves accordingly, or it can be recorded as a pictograph on the wall. Add up the totals to ensure that the correct number of children are recorded.

If you collect the school dinner money, ask the children to work in tens, counting up the number of ten pence pieces to make up a pound. Older children might be able to add up other coins and work out change.

You can then move on to look at lunch boxes. Before opening them, sort them out into colours and make a real-life block graph by piling them up on the floor. They could then be classified in another way, for example, by the characters shown on the lids, or whether the box has the child's name on it. This can lead to other questions. Is there a most popular colour, and if so, why? What is the best way to store lunch boxes?

Ask the children to look inside their lunch boxes and list the different items found there. Are there any foods that are common to all the lunch boxes? The children could then discuss how specific their classifications should be. For example, should sandwiches made from white and brown bread be classified separately? Without necessarily using the word 'average', talk about what most people have for lunch.

Follow-up
● Relate the children's findings on the contents of their lunch boxes to an investigation of the different kinds of food the body needs.
● Look at the design of lunch boxes and keep a record over a period of time of any accidents which happen with lunch boxes. Can the children suggest better alternative designs that will reduce the risk of accidents?

2. School lunches

Age range
Five to seven.

Group size
Individuals or small groups.

What you need
Graph paper.

What to do
Ask the children to carry out a survey to discover the most popular school lunch. This information could be represented in a block graph or in a mapping diagram, linking children's names to their favourite food.

It is interesting to find out whether the children's favourite school lunch is actually their favourite meal of all. If it isn't, the children could write to the school meals service, identifying a gap in the market.

The information about favourite school lunches could also be represented in a different way. Use artificial food from the class shop or let the children make models to show their findings, with each model representing a favourite food. For example, each model could stand for five people, and the models could be arranged on a huge dinner plate of favourite foods.

The children could also create a data trail showing what happens from the point when children identify their preference for a school meal to the point at which it ends up on a plate in front of them. Does their preference go to the school secretary first, and then to the kitchen? What does the cook do with the information? How does she plan to make the correct amount of food? This allows children to see the relationship between mathematical facts and the choices and decisions that need to be made.

Follow-up
Set up a survey of favourite school meals across the school. Is it practical to interview every child in the school? If not, who will be interviewed? This introduces the idea of a sample.

3. Cutting and peeling

Age range
Six to seven.

Group size
Individuals or pairs.

What you need
Pieces of fruit, such as apples and oranges, a knife, a peeler, tape-measures, scales.

What to do
Cutting up a piece of fruit provides many mathematical possibilities. In the majority of cases, the cutting and peeling will be done by an adult, but the children should still be given the opportunity to make the mathematical decisions themselves.

Peel the apple. If it is peeled in one long strip, how long will the peel be? This is an interesting question for discussion and estimation. Can the children think of any way of making an intelligent estimate? How do they measure the length of the peel? Ask them to weigh the piece of fruit before and after it has been peeled. What is the difference? They might also do a survey among the teachers to find out how they would peel an apple. Is there any connection between the way the apple is peeled and the amount of peel at the end?

Cut up the apple into three or four equal pieces. Ask the children what each piece will be called. If you cut each piece again, how many pieces will there be? As an orange is already in segments the children will be able to divide it into sections themselves. Ask them to count the number of segments. Do they think that other oranges of the same shape and size have the same number of segments?

Follow-up
- Ask the children to describe in words the different techniques used for peeling an apple or orange.
- Ask them to measure the amount of juice squeezed from an orange.
- Let them compare the weight of an orange before and after squeezing.
- Look together at the packaging in which fruit is sold.
- Examine the relationship between imperial and metric units.

4. A loaf of bread

Age range
Seven to nine.

Group size
Pairs.

What you need
A loaf of packaged, sliced bread, scales, a toaster, calculators.

What to do
A loaf of bread has many mathematical possibilities. Ask the children to begin by looking at the label and ingredients. How far over or under the use-by date is the loaf of bread? Then ask the children to count the number of slices of bread in the loaf. If they divide the price by the number of slices, how much does each slice cost? They should try to estimate the cost first. They can then weigh a slice of bread. If this weight is multiplied by the number of slices in the loaf, does it add up to the total weight displayed on the packaging? If not, why not? The children could make up their own problems. For example, how many sandwiches could be made out of the loaf, if each sandwich requires two slices?

What happens when bread is toasted? The children could compare the weight of a slice of bread before and after toasting, and older children could work out the percentage decrease in weight. They could use reference books to try to find an explanation for this weight loss. The children could also work out how long it would take to toast the whole loaf by timing how long it takes to toast one slice of bread. What if their toaster toasts more than one slice of bread at a time?

Follow-up
This sort of activity can take place any time when ingredients are being used for cooking in school. Look together at labels, weigh ingredients, compare cooked and uncooked weights and examine prices.

5. Food diary

Age range
Seven to nine.

Group size
Individuals.

What you need
Photocopiable page 125.

What to do
Encourage the children to keep a diary of all the food they eat during the week. Contact their parents and ask

for their assistance in completing photocopiable page 125. As the children will eat more food at home than at school, it is probably better that the sheet is sent home and completed there. The children can keep a note of what they eat at school and record it when they get home.

When the week is over, ask the children to bring their photocopiable sheets back into school and analyse their data. Ask them questions such as:
• What is the total number of meals eaten over a week by the children in the class?
• What is the average number of courses eaten by children at their main meal?
• Using a tally sheet, what meal appears most often during the week?
• Taking one day's meals and visiting a local shop, how much does the food cost for that day?

Follow-up
Repeat this activity at different times of the year to see if seasonal patterns emerge.

6. Food shapes

Age range
Seven to nine.

Group size
Individuals.

What you need
A range of foodstuffs and food packages of different shapes.

What to do
This activity can be done in two ways. One way is to provide the children with a range of foods and packages and a number of shape name and picture labels. The children can then sort out each foodstuff or package into the correct shape category.

Another way is to provide the children with the foodstuffs and packages without using shape labels and

ask them to sort out the shapes the best way they can. Ask them to describe which two-dimensional shapes are needed to make up the three-dimensional shapes. For example, to make up a cylinder you would need two circles and a rectangle, whereas to make up a cube you would need six squares.

What about shapes that are not regular, but look similar to regular shapes? It is worth letting the children sort out all the shapes without giving them any guidance. Should they include the similar shapes with the regular shapes? Or should they create a new category of non-regular shapes that they are unable to classify? If they create a new category, ask them to describe the features of the non-regular shapes and decide which regular shape each is most like.

Follow-up
• The children could be given a foodstuff and asked to design appropriate packaging which is both functional and economic.
• They could look at how foods are currently packaged and think of alternatives.

7. Labels

Age range
Seven to eleven.

Group size
Individuals or pairs.

What you need
Clean, empty food tins, cartons and boxes with labels. Include similar products in different sizes and prices, such as a 200g tin of beans and a 400g tin of beans.

What to do
Food packets and boxes display a range of information. First of all ask the children to look at the price. Many products will no longer have price labels on them but will have a bar code. Ask them to consider the advantages and disadvantages of such a system. They can then look carefully at the bar codes. Do these codes always contain the same number of lines and digits? The children could add up the numbers under the bar codes and see which one comes to the highest total. If the products do have the price on them, ask the children to compare the prices of two similar products which are in different sized tins. They need to be able to work out the cost per gram to see which represents better value for money. However, if the products are made by two different manufacturers, is the cost per unit the sole determinant? How can they quantify quality? Is something always better because it costs less (or more)?

Ask the children to look at the ingredients and the nutritional information. In isolation, does this information make much sense? Take two similar sized tins of beans and compare the labels. This works well if one contains low-calorie beans. You could then ask:

- What is the proportion of fat per 100g?
- How much sugar does each tin contain?
- What proportion of the contents of the tin are the beans themselves?

Finally, ask the children whether or not the label provides all the information they need. For example, having the ingredients listed might be useful, but might it not be more helpful to know in what proportion?

Follow-up
If the children are using the tins and packets in cookery work, ask them to explain how the contents need to be prepared and cooked, by reading the cooking instructions.

8. Making a meal of it

Age range
Nine to eleven.

Group size
Individuals or pairs.

What you need
Ingredients chosen by the children to make a meal, cutlery and crockery, a cooker, a calculator.

What to do
This activity is likely to require the assistance of an adult helper. Individuals or pairs of children in the class can be asked to plan and prepare a meal from scratch for somebody of their choice. The children need to begin by ascertaining when the person they would like to invite is available at lunchtime. Having worked that out, they need to prepare a timetable which takes into account when an adult helper will be available, what ingredients and materials they need and how long the meal will take to prepare and cook on the day. They also need to plan what they can afford. (Perhaps the school would be able to subsidise each pair of children and then allow the children to provide additional money or ingredients.) On the day when the meal is to be prepared, the adult helper could take the children to the local shops to buy their ingredients. The children will clearly have to look for value for money given that they are working to a tight budget. They will also need to have planned their morning to ensure that everything is done before their visitor arrives.

When they get back to school, they can prepare the meal and set out the table with the correct cutlery and crockery. Hopefully, their preparations will have gone according to plan and the meal can be served on time. After the meal, the children can record all their expenditure and assess whether they could have prepared the same meal more cheaply. They should also examine their timetable and find out whether or not they could have made better use of their time.

Follow-up
If the same meal had been eaten by four or eight people, or by the whole class, how much would it have cost? Would it necessarily be a case of multiplying the number of people by the cost of the meal? Would bulk-buying and discounts make any difference?

9. A visit to the bakery

Age range
Nine to eleven.

Group size
Small groups or the whole class.

What you need
A local bakery or supermarket bakery willing to accommodate the children, calculators, scrap paper.

What to do
Arrange a visit to the local bakery and give the children an introduction to mathematics in a variety of practical ways. Ask the children to look at how the bakery calculates how much of every ingredient it needs each day. Using this information, they could calculate the number of ingredients and their cost over a week or a year. Look too at the range of shapes in the bakery and ask the children to record how many they see. They could also examine how the different shapes are made in the dough using shape cutters. How much wastage is

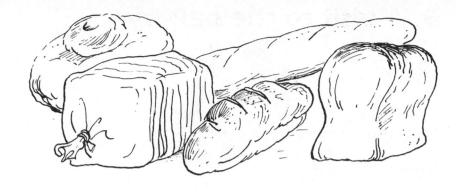

there with irregular shapes? The children could experiment on this for themselves when they return to the school, using Plasticine and shape cutters.

How is food moved out of the bakery? Are loaves laid on trays? If so, the children could count how many loaves are put on a tray and then work out how many loaves would be on six trays or ten trays. They could ask how many loaves leave the bakery in a day so that they can do weekly, monthly or annual calculations. The children could ask for the cooking times of different products such as loaves, cream cakes, sponges and so on. They could also find the highest and lowest temperatures that products are cooked at.

When the children return to school, they could amass all the different facts they have gathered from the bakery and present them under the heading 'Did you know . . .?' or 'Twenty interesting facts about the local bakery'. Don't forget to ask the children to find out some facts of their own.

Follow-up
If you are able to visit a number of shops, you could build up a fact-file. It is then worth asking the children how they would use such facts. Are they interesting in themselves or could they have some practical use?

10. Menus

Age range
Nine to eleven.

Group size
Individuals.

What you need
Menus from restaurants, photocopiable page 126.

What to do
Send for or collect a range of children's and adults' menus from different restaurants. Ask the children to make some initial comparisons. How restricted is the range of options on the children's menu? This could be calculated by counting the number of meals on each menu and working out the difference expressed in percentage terms. Ask the children to look at the prices as well. Do any items appear on both menus? What are the relative prices? Use photocopiable page 126 to ask the children a range of questions about the menus. Finally, the children can choose and calculate the cost of meals, perhaps within a budget.

Follow-up
Using the answers the children have provided, average costs of favourite meals could be worked out.

Classroom display ideas

- Using data from the school dinner register, prepare large-scale line graphs showing the numbers of school meals and packed lunches eaten over a given period.
- Make a three-dimensional lunch box display and fill it with models of the typical contents based on an analysis of the class's lunch boxes.
- Display a data trail of the information needed to prepare the correct number of school lunches starting from the time the children decide to have a lunch, to the time the lunch is served.
- Use fabrics to represent the lengths of apple or orange peelings. The longest and shortest lengths can be displayed.
- Create a large-scale food package label and identify the range of information on it. Make a display of as many different kinds of labels as the children can find.
- Make a clay loaf of bread to display findings gathered in Activity 4.
- Display the children's food diaries. Include the food diaries of teachers as well.
- Put up a block graph of the children's favourite foods.
- Make a display of food shape silhouettes and ask visitors to the classroom to identify the foodstuffs.
- Prepare a collage display of each child's favourite meal, with approximate costings attached.

Links with other curriculum areas

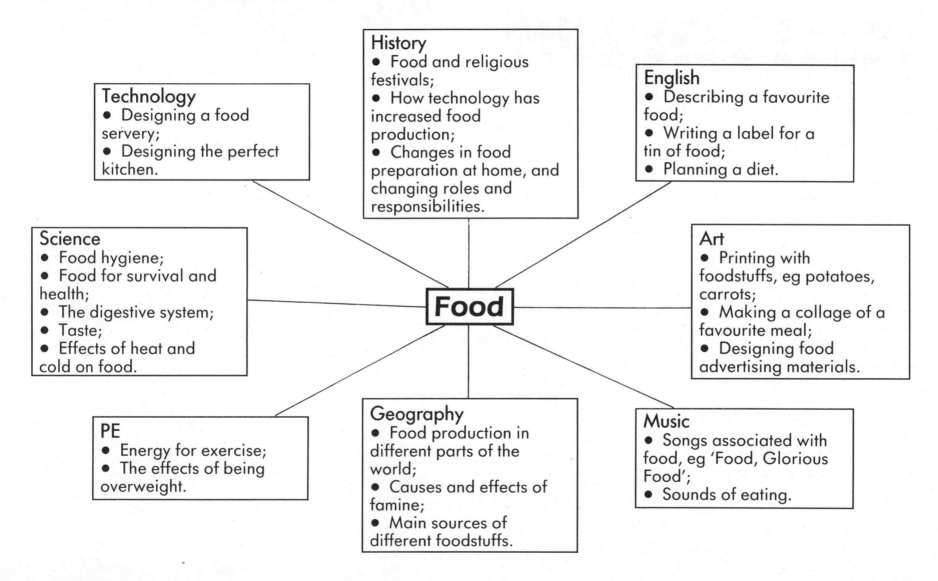

Technology
- Designing a food servery;
- Designing the perfect kitchen.

History
- Food and religious festivals;
- How technology has increased food production;
- Changes in food preparation at home, and changing roles and responsibilities.

English
- Describing a favourite food;
- Writing a label for a tin of food;
- Planning a diet.

Science
- Food hygiene;
- Food for survival and health;
- The digestive system;
- Taste;
- Effects of heat and cold on food.

Food

Art
- Printing with foodstuffs, eg potatoes, carrots;
- Making a collage of a favourite meal;
- Designing food advertising materials.

PE
- Energy for exercise;
- The effects of being overweight.

Geography
- Food production in different parts of the world;
- Causes and effects of famine;
- Main sources of different foodstuffs.

Music
- Songs associated with food, eg 'Food, Glorious Food';
- Sounds of eating.

Reproducible material

At the supermarket, see page 13

Customer survey

Male/female (delete as appropriate)

Age:
  Under 20
  20-30
  30-40
  40+

How often do you shop here?
  More than once a week
  Once a week
  Once a month
  Other

Do you live:
  Within one mile of the store?
  Between one and five miles from the store?
  Further than five miles from the store?

How do you get to this store?
  By car
  By bus
  By taxi
  On foot

Why do you shop in this store?
  Nearest to your home
  Best in the area
  Always shopped here
  Other

What do you particularly like about this store?

What do you dislike about this store?

Can you think of any improvements?

This page may be photocopied for use in the classroom and should not be declared in any return in respect of any photocopying licence.

Shopping survey, see page 17

Your shopping centre							
Name	Owner	Service	Time in this shop	Age range of customers	Most popular time	Opening and closing times	Any special features

This page may be photocopied for use in the classroom and should not be declared in any return in respect of any photocopying licence.

Around the houses, see page 25

Here are some flat and three-dimensional shapes you will see when walking around near the school.
Name each shape and then draw on it to make it look like an object you have seen.

This page may be photocopied for use in the classroom and should not be declared in any return in respect of any photocopying licence.

Town trail, see page 25

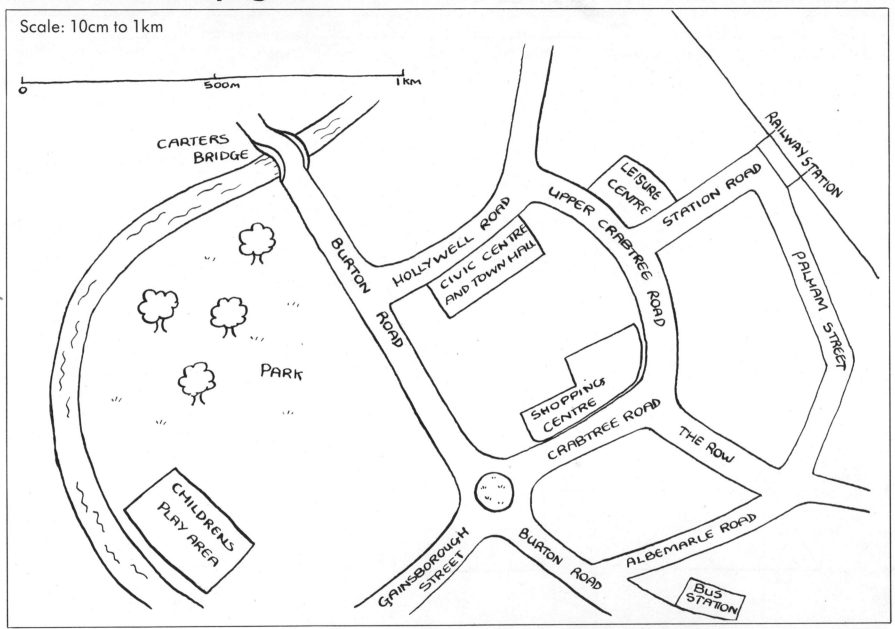

Scale: 10cm to 1km

0   500M   1KM

CARTERS BRIDGE

PARK

CHILDRENS PLAY AREA

BURTON ROAD

HOLLYWELL ROAD

CIVIC CENTRE AND TOWN HALL

UPPER CRABTREE ROAD

LEISURE CENTRE

STATION ROAD

RAILWAY STATION

PALMAM STREET

SHOPPING CENTRE

CRABTREE ROAD

THE ROW

GAINSBOROUGH STREET

BURTON ROAD

ALBEMARLE ROAD

BUS STATION

This page may be photocopied for use in the classroom and should not be declared in any return in respect of any photocopying licence.

Road traffic survey, see page 27

Date _____ Time: From _____ To _____	Cars	Emergency service vehicles	Vans	Lorries	Buses	Motorbikes	Bicycles	Other vehicles	Total vehicles

This page may be photocopied for use in the classroom and should not be declared in any return in respect of any photocopying licence.

The view from above, see page 39

Here are some household objects seen from above. Can you draw the same object from another angle?

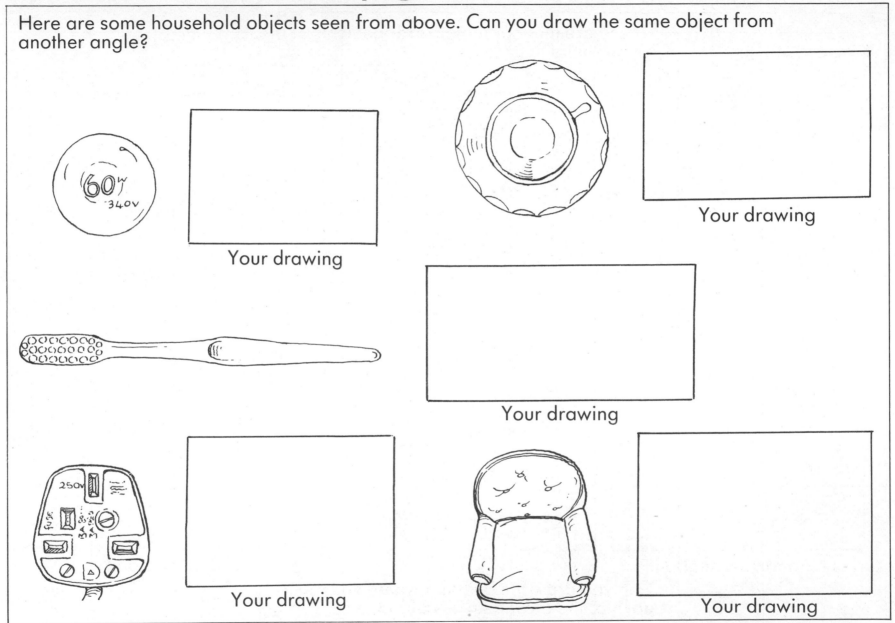

Your drawing

Your drawing

Your drawing

Your drawing

Your drawing

This page may be photocopied for use in the classroom and should not be declared in any return in respect of any photocopying licence.

Bricks, see page 41

These are the four major arrangements of bricks
to be found in Britain.

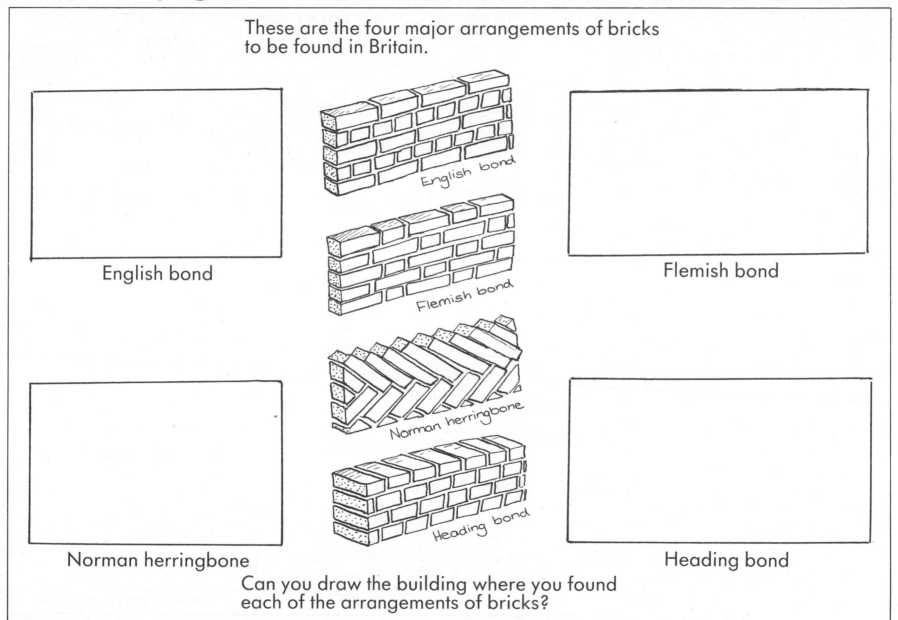

English bond

Flemish bond

Norman herringbone

Heading bond

Can you draw the building where you found
each of the arrangements of bricks?

This page may be photocopied for use in the classroom and should not be declared in any return in respect of any photocopying licence.

Around the town, see page 50

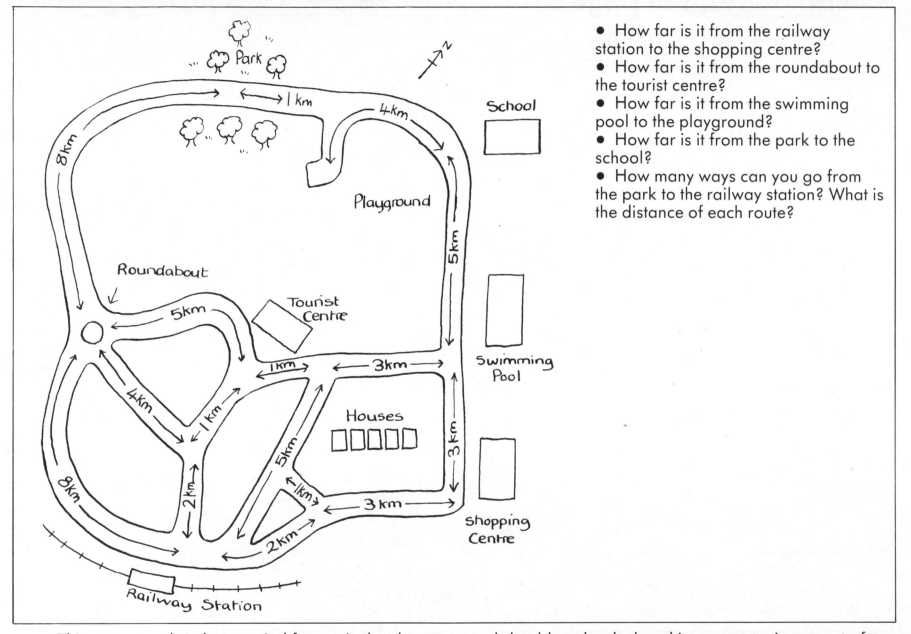

- How far is it from the railway station to the shopping centre?
- How far is it from the roundabout to the tourist centre?
- How far is it from the swimming pool to the playground?
- How far is it from the park to the school?
- How many ways can you go from the park to the railway station? What is the distance of each route?

This page may be photocopied for use in the classroom and should not be declared in any return in respect of any photocopying licence.

Going places, see page 53

This is a distance chart to show how far it is from one place to another. Distances are given in miles.

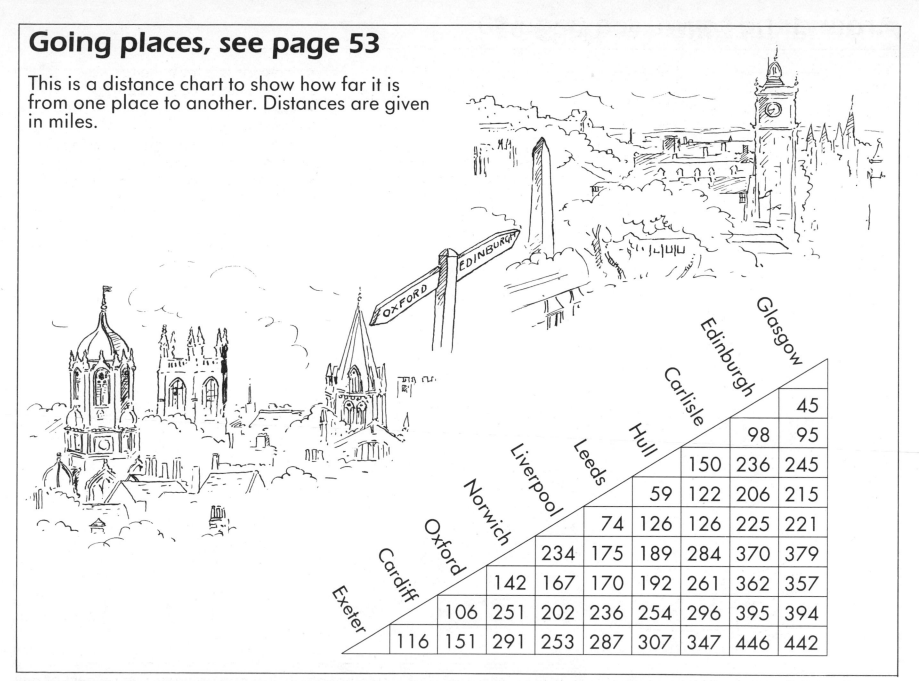

	Exeter	Cardiff	Oxford	Norwich	Liverpool	Leeds	Hull	Carlisle	Edinburgh	Glasgow
Glasgow										45
Edinburgh									98	95
Carlisle								150	236	245
Hull							59	122	206	215
Leeds						74	126	126	225	221
Liverpool					234	175	189	284	370	379
Norwich				142	167	170	192	261	362	357
Oxford			106	251	202	236	254	296	395	394
Cardiff		116	151	291	253	287	307	347	446	442

This page may be photocopied for use in the classroom and should not be declared in any return in respect of any photocopying licence.

Personal fact-file, see page 65

Name:

Age: ——— years ——— months.

Height:

Estimate ——— m ——— cm

Actual ——— m ——— cm

Weight:

Estimate ——— kg ——— g

Actual ——— kg ——— g

Activity profile

- I can run 50m in ——— seconds.

- I can do ——— bench jumps in a minute.

- I can do ——— sit-ups in a minute.

- I can do a standing long-jump of ——— m ——— cm.

- I can throw a cricket ball ——— m ——— cm.

This page may be photocopied for use in the classroom and should not be declared in any return in respect of any photocopying licence.

Fields and pitches, see page 67

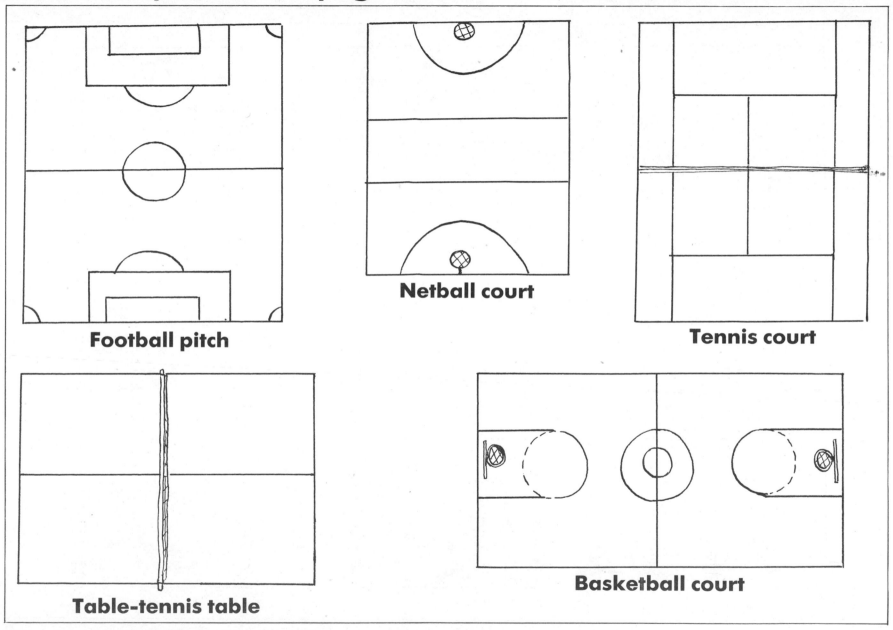

Football pitch

Netball court

Tennis court

Table-tennis table

Basketball court

This page may be photocopied for use in the classroom and should not be declared in any return in respect of any photocopying licence.

Picture time, see page 75

This page may be photocopied for use in the classroom and should not be declared in any return in respect of any photocopying licence.

The calendar, see page 78

January

February

March

April

May

June

July

August

September

October

November

December

This page may be photocopied for use in the classroom and should not be declared in any return in respect of any photocopying licence.

Stars and 'arithmestars', see page 91

Fill in the empty circles so that the numbers along each line add up to the same total. The total for star 1 is different from the total for star 2.

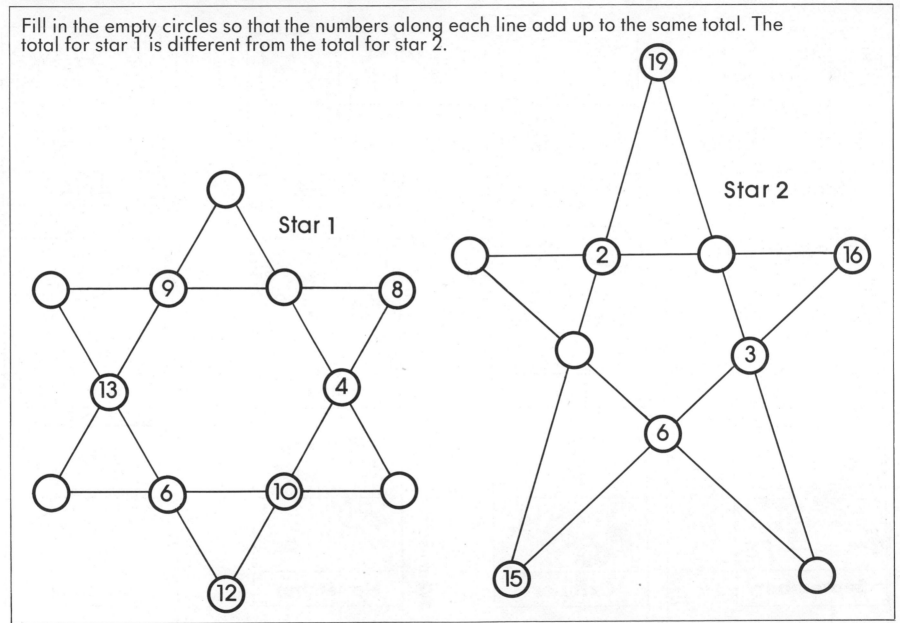

Star 1

Star 2

This page may be photocopied for use in the classroom and should not be declared in any return in respect of any photocopying licence.

Food diary, see page 102

Day	Breakfast	Lunch	Tea/dinner	Other snacks
Monday				
Tuesday				
Wednesday				
Thursday				
Friday				

This page may be photocopied for use in the classroom and should not be declared in any return in respect of any photocopying licence.

Menus, see page 107

Menus, see page 107

How much change would you have from £5.00 if you had a Fisherman's Friend and a Cold Comfort?

Plan and cost out a meal for two children.

How many Bangers Specials could you get for £5.00, and how much change would there be?

How much would four milks cost?

Children's menu

Main meals

Bangers Special (sausage and beans)	£1.50
Fisherman's Friend (fish and chips)	£1.75
Vegetable Variety (vegetarian lasagne)	£2.00
Salad Special (cheese salad)	£1.50
Burger Bun (hamburger and chips)	£2.00
Extra chips	£0.50

Desserts

Cold Comfort (ice-cream in three flavours)	£1.00
Banana Blitz (banana and ice-cream)	£1.25
Pancake Pie	£1.25

Drinks

Cola	£0.70
Milk	£0.70
Orange	£0.70

Which meal costs more – a Vegetarian Variety and a Pancake Pie or a Salad Special and a Cold Comfort?

What would two colas and an orange cost?

What would a Salad Special, an Extra Chips, a Banana Blitz and a cola cost?

This page may be photocopied for use in the classroom and should not be declared in any return in respect of any photocopying licence.

Attainment target chart

Use the chart on the following page to help match up the activities outlined in this book with the relevant National Curriculum attainment targets for mathematics. The activities are identified by numbers; thus **2/9** is Chapter 2, activity 9.

For the purposes of the chart we have used the attainment targets put forward in *Mathematics for Ages 5 to 16* (DES/WO 1991), the proposals of the Secretary of State for Education and Science and the Secretary of State for Wales published in May 1991. Attainment Target 1 is 'Using and applying mathematics'; AT2 is 'Number'; AT3 is 'Algebra'; AT4 is 'Shape and space'; and AT5 is 'Handling data'.

Level \ AT	1	2	3	4	5
1	1/10, 3/5, 5/2, 6/3, 8/1	1/1, 1/10, 2/2, 3/5, 5/3, 6/3, 7/3, 8/1, 8/3	5/1	1/2, 2/1, 2/2, 2/3, 3/4, 4/1, 4/2, 4/3, 5/2, 7/2, 8/3, 8/6	3/1, 3/2, 3/3, 5/4, 7/1, 8/1, 8/2
2	1/10, 6/3, 6/5, 8/1	1/1-3, 1/5, 1/10, 2/2, 3/5, 5/3, 6/1-5, 7/3, 8/1, 8/3		1/2-5, 1/10, 4/1-3, 5/2, 7/2, 7/5, 8/3, 8/6, 8/9	1/5, 3/1-3, 5/4, 8/1, 8/2
3	1/5, 1/10, 2/7, 6/5, 6/7, 6/8	1/5, 1/10, 2/9, 3/9, 5/5, 5/9, 6/2-5, 6/8, 7/4-5, 7/8-9, 8/4-5, 8/9-10	2/7, 5/6, 5/10	1/4, 1/5, 2/5, 2/7, 4/4, 5/7, 7/2, 7/5, 8/6, 8/9	1/5, 5/9, 8/2
4	1/5, 1/10, 2/7, 2/9-10, 3/9, 4/6, 5/5-6, 5/8-9, 6/7-8, 7/14, 7/6, 7/9, 8/7, 8/10	1/5-6, 1/9-10, 2/9, 3/9, 4/6, 4/8, 5/5, 5/8-10, 6/6, 6/8, 6/10, 7/4-6, 7/8-10, 8/4-5, 8/8-10	5/6, 5/10	2/5, 2/7, 3/6-8, 5/7, 7/7, 7/10, 8/6, 8/9	1/5, 2/6, 2/10, 4/8-9, 5/5, 5/9, 5/11, 6/9, 7/4
5	1/5, 1/7, 1/10, 2/6, 2/10, 3/10, 4/7-8, 4/10, 5/5, 5/8-9, 6/9-10, 7/4, 7/9, 8/7, 8/10	1/6, 1/9-10, 2/4, 2/8, 3/9, 3/11, 4/4, 4/6-9, 5/5, 5/8-10, 6/10, 7/4, 7/6, 7/8-10, 8/4, 8/7-8	1/9, 5/10	2/7, 3/7, 3/8, 3/10, 7/10	1/8, 2/6, 2/10, 4/8-9, 5/5, 5/9, 5/11, 6/9
6	1/7, 1/10, 2/6, 2/10, 4/10, 5/8-9, 7/10, 8/7	1/9-10, 3/9, 3/11, 4/6-9, 5/5, 7/6, 8/7-8		2/8, 3/7, 3/10, 4/5	2/10, 4/9, 5/5, 5/11, 6/9